Forewo|

By Professor Aubrey 1

In the Preface, Chris Mitchell himself asks whether we need any more Lake District guides – there are certainly plenty of them. What do we need to enjoy this delectable part of the British Isles? Perhaps nothing, just wander at will drinking in the exhilaration of the scenery, the bitter smell of peaty soil, the roar of the becks, with just a map to bring you home again. At times this is absolutely enough and its own reward. But then questions are bound to spring into mind as one's eyes move over the landscape. Questions about the different landforms and rocks, the patterns of vegetation and the patterns of human settlements, many of the remote ones, ruinous now. In the mountainous parts of Britain the history of human activity is now closely bound to the vegetation which has moved back, covering and softening where once people grew crops or drove cattle or mined for lead. A little of the right kind of observation will enable you to build up a history, and the biology of the situation often has a fascination of its own as you discover how varied life has exploited the new opportunities human activity has provided.

Chris Mitchell here provides an extraordinary mix of guided observation and, having given just enough information, poses questions which invite solution, even providing 'answers' at the end! As is the norm with guides today, it suggests a series of excursions, the required maps, timings, which pubs will feed you, etc., but there the similarity ends. Here the author wants us to look much more closely to see what is almost always completely ignored and then use what we shall find to construct a history. The unique flavour of this guide owes much to its author's fascination with some of the least considered of our vegetation – lichens. Ubiquitous in the countryside, admired sometimes for the lovely colours and textures they impart to rock, but in Chris Mitchell's hands capable of weaving complex stories about geology and more recent history. This is an intensely personal set of proposed excursions into both familiar and much less familiar parts of the Lakes. It is quirky and often quite demanding, but I shall be surprised if it doesn't win many converts. A highly innovative and original guide, it is eye-opening in the very best sense of the phrase.

Aubrey Manning

Preface

'Is there room for another guide book on the Lake District? ...'

The challenge was to present a book that would make the experienced visitor see the area in a completely new light. But what could possibly be said that hasn't already been said about Castlerigg Stone Circle, the Fairfield Horseshoe or the shoreline walk around Buttermere? Here was the first challenge: to make the familiar appear fresh – as though visited for the first time.

The second challenge was to create a popular, easy-to-follow guidebook that dealt with academic topics so often hidden under complex methods and dusty Latin names. Geology may have inspired William Blake 'to see infinity in a grain of sand', but how do you make lichen exciting? How do you make such specialist topics accessible without compromising the science?

Perhaps the only way is to catch the reader unawares. Subterfuge, artifice, circumvention: I admit to it all, if only in a good cause. And so be warned – you read this book at your peril! You may have inadvertently picked it off the shelf thinking it to be a good armchair-read; perhaps mistaking it for a compendium of modern-day Sherlock Holmes stories. But after Chapter 1, you will be speaking in Latin. By Chapter 9, you will have stopped walking and taken to crawling with a hand lens. And by the end, all hope will have gone – and you will have joined the British Lichen Society!

Acknowledgements

This book would not have been possible without the help of many people.

My thanks to Geoff Medd (National Trust, Beckfoot) for checking details of the walk through Holme Wood; Bill Veitch (former Instructor with the Army's Driving and Maintenance School, Keswick) for providing historical details of 'Wading in Buttermere'. Thanks also to Geoff Wilson for supplying a video copy of the original cine-film of the Army training at Buttermere and Devoke Water. (Despite extensive searches

LAKE DISTRICT NATURAL HISTORY WALKS

Case Notes of a Nature Detective

Christopher Mitchell

To Sarah and John

Published by Sigma Leisure – an imprint of
Sigma Press, 5 Alton Road, Wilmslow, Cheshire SK9 5DY, England.

British Library Cataloguing in Publication Data
A CIP record for this book is available from the British Library.

ISBN: 1-85058-807-4

Typesetting and Design by: Sigma Press, Wilmslow, Cheshire.

Cover photograph: Fly agaric – Buttermere, October 2003

Photographs, Maps and Illustrations: © Christopher Mitchell unless otherwise indicated. Maps are based on Ordnance Survey maps: 1st edition 1:10 000 (1848-1868); 2nd edition 1:10 000 (1891-1901); 1:63 360 (1948). Reproduced by kind permission of the Ordnance Survey.

Printed by: Ashford Colour Press Ltd

Disclaimer: Care should always be taken when walking in hill country. Where appropriate, attention has been drawn to matters of safety. The author and publisher cannot take responsibility for any accidents or injury incurred whilst following these walks. Only you can judge your own fitness, competence and experience. Do not rely solely on sketch maps for navigation: we strongly recommend the use of appropriate Ordnance Survey (or equivalent) maps.

through National Film and Imperial War Museum Archives, the source of the original cine-film could not be found.)

My thanks also to David Fraser (English Heritage) for providing me with the Draft Report of the Castlerigg Stone Circle, Vanessa Winchester (School of Geography, University of Oxford) for help and advice on lichenometry and for supplying lichen growth curves from churchyards at Crosthwaite and the Vale of St John, Sandy and Brian Coppins (British Lichen Society) for their encouragement and for their lichen data, and Alan Orange (National Museum of Wales) for help with lichen identification. Thanks also to Don Smith (British Lichen Society) for providing his lichen lists for the Cumbrian churches, and to John Duffus (The Edinburgh Centre for Toxicology) for advice and suggestions on the Coniston walk.

I am particularly grateful to Alan Smith (President of the Cumberland Geological Society) for help with rock identification at specific sites and for providing background information on the geology of the area.

I would also like to thank Stephen Hewitt (Tullie House Museum) for help with the identification of otter spraints; Anne Baker, Fred Naggs and Paul Hillyard (the Natural History Museum) for identifying difficult invertebrates; Derrick Holdsworth (Cumbria measurer for the Tree Register of the British Isles) for information on 'Champion Trees'; Neil Robinson for information on ant populations and for identifying various samples; David Millward (British Geological Survey) for information on Kailpot Crag; Jamie Quartermaine (Oxford Archaeology North) for details of the Lancaster Archaeology Unit Surveys at Haweswater; and Bette Hopkins (Cumbria Sites and Monuments Record Officer) for once again supplying information from the County Records.

The pilot study of the Dovedale trees involved many people. My thanks to Stephen Dowson (National Trust, Watermillock) for arranging permission to obtain the leaf samples; Tony Hutchings and Ned Cundall (Forest Research, Alice Holt Lodge and Roslin) for advice on experimental design, and Geoff Collins (former head gardener, Inverewe) for identifying difficult plant material. A special thank you goes to Mark Hodson and Anne Dudley (Department of Soil Science, School of Human and Environmental Sciences, University of Reading) for analysing the leaf samples.

I would especially like to thank Howard and Ruth Holden for their company on several walks, and for their efforts in revisiting sites to obtain 'difficult' photographs. Howard also helped in preparing and scanning much of the photographic material. He was also responsible for producing the first-published images of the Army's D-Day training at Buttermere and Devoke Water.

Two people, in particular, helped me in gathering my research materials: Anthony Fletcher (British Lichen Society Librarian) and Eleanor Kingston (Lake District National Park Authority Archaeologist). Their help in photocopying numerous articles and reports was invaluable in the preparation of this book.

Thanks also to Phil and Heather Lyon for the loan of maps and books, Denton Pryor for the Dictaphone, and Mike and Cathy Mortimer for their company, help and suggestions.

On the technical side, a special thank you to Robert Arnold for introducing me to computer graphics, and for help with the maps and photomacrographs. His role as a trouble-shooter whenever I got into 'computing difficulties' was greatly appreciated.

One of the most enjoyable parts of writing this book has been using Keswick as our base whilst researching the walks. My wife and myself would like to give our thanks to Freda Hayes for being such a splendid 'landlady' and friend during our many visits.

Finally, I thank my wife Janet, for all her help, advice and perseverance during what has been a most enjoyable project.

Please Note

Many of the walks include Sites of Special Scientific Interest (SSSIs), Regionally Important Geological and Geomorphological Sites (RIGS), or Scheduled Ancient Monuments. Please keep their disturbance to a minimum and leave plants, rock faces and mineral sites as you found them for others to see.

The features mentioned in these walks will change naturally over time. If you think these changes should be included in the next edition, I should be most grateful if you would inform the publisher.

Chris Mitchell

Contents

Location Map

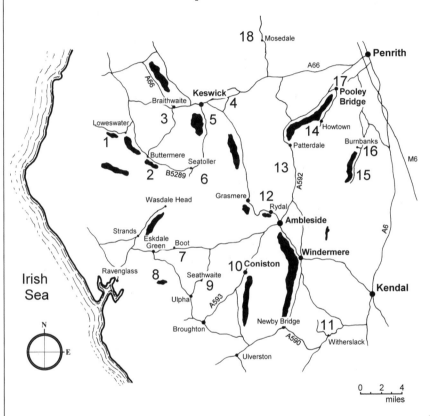

18 Mosedale

Penrith

A66

17 Pooley Bridge

Keswick

Braithwaite

4

Loweswater

3

5

14 Howtown

Patterdale

Burnbanks

16

M6

1

Buttermere

Seatoller

B5289

2

6

13

15

Wasdale Head

Grasmere

12

Rydal

Ambleside

A592

A6

Strands

Eskdale Green

Boot

7

Windermere

Ravenglass

8

Seathwaite

9

10 Coniston

Irish Sea

Ulpha

A593

Kendal

N

Broughton

Newby Bridge

11

Witherslack

E

Ulverston

A590

0 2 4
miles

1. Loweswater	10. Coniston
2. Buttermere	11. Whitbarrow
3. Newlands Valley	12. Fairfield
4. Castlerigg Stone Circle	13. Dovedale
5. Walla Crag	14. Hallin Fell
6. Combe Gill	15. Haweswater
7. Eskdale	16. Thornthwaite Force
8. Devoke Water	17. Pooley Bridge
9. Duddon Valley	18. Carrock Fell

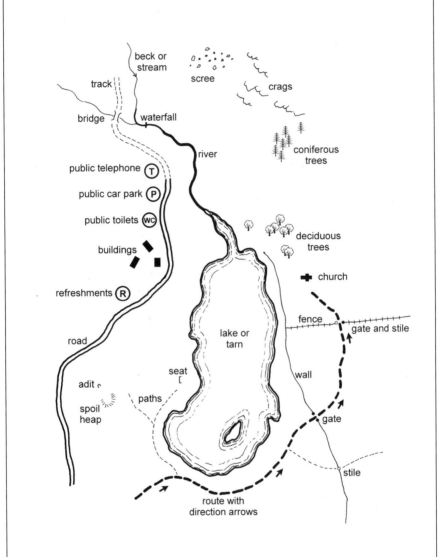

beck or stream

track

bridge

waterfall

scree

crags

coniferous trees

river

public telephone (T)

public car park (P)

public toilets (WC)

deciduous trees

buildings

church

refreshments (R)

fence

gate and stile

road

lake or tarn

wall

seat

adit

paths

spoil heap

gate

stile

route with direction arrows

Map Symbols

Introduction

"... to see the Lakes clearly... we must penetrate the living landscape behind the view. We must get out of our cars, feel the rock under our feet, breathe the Cumbrian air, and learn to know something, at least, of the complex organic life of grass, herb and tree..." (Norman Nicholson, *Looking at the Lakes*: National Park Guide No 6, 1975)

A Different Kind of Guide Book

This book explores some of the Lake District's lesser-known aspects of natural history – to see what lies hidden behind the scenery. It contains 18 walks completed between April 2002 and October 2003. The information has been written-up in the form of case notes that can be used as a practical field guide, or enjoyed as a series of detective stories from the comfort of your armchair.

Being a nature detective often means focusing on the fleeting detail. The risk is that it can all change so quickly. If you stand on Scafell Pike and list the surrounding hills as seen from the summit cairn, the description will be valid a week later. But if you were to look at the cairn itself and focus on the highest point – where there are streaks of birdlime, four inches long and coloured purple, left by ravens that have been eating bilberries – then the chance of seeing this next week is considerably reduced! Success will depend upon many factors: the time of year (bilberries are ripe in July and August); the prevailing wind direction (affecting where the birds will land); the rainfall over the past 24 hours (determining whether or not the rocks will be washed clean); and the number of people visiting the summit (keeping the birds away and disturbing the cairn). At least the Isle of Man stays put!

From a nature detective's point of view, the challenge is to seek out the detail and then interpret what it means. What has caused an animal to behave in a certain way? Why does the vegetation change below a Bronze Age cairn? What has caused a patch of rushes to bend in a particular direction? This is not about getting to the top just to admire the view. You enter each walk as a forensic scientist about to enter a crime scene!

It is all down to scientific deduction. When Sherlock Holmes said, 'Elementary, my dear Watson!' – he meant it. On the face of it, however, the solving of complex puzzles appears to require special powers: 'the seeing eye' as it is sometimes called. But when Holmes explains how the owner of a mislaid pipe is a left-handed man with good teeth, the initial surprise disappears as the simple logic is revealed.

Interpreting the countryside brings together many scientific disciplines. For example, the geology of an area will affect the type of plant life you are likely to encounter. Limestone pavement has a completely different flora to that found on volcanic rock. The geology also affects the animal population. You are more likely to find 14 and 16 point antlers in red deer grazing on limestone than in red deer found in the central fells. In fact, antlers from animals in the Thirlmere area are softer than normal and, once cast, are more likely to have their points eaten away by the deer themselves as they try to make up for the lack of calcium in their diet (Mitchell and Delap, 1974).

It is regular patterns of behaviour that leave their signs on the ground. The next time you pass through the first gate after leaving the car park at the start of a walk, look at the stone wall alongside the opening. Invariably, a patch of yellow lichen will be found extending to a height of half a metre from the ground. To solve the puzzle, watch your dog as you approach the wall.

Field studies as a Forensic Challenge

Field studies should be fun – an exercise in lateral thinking, skipping lightly across the different disciplines, then standing back to get an over-all view. Intuitions, relationships, chains of events – these are what provide the challenge and the excitement of field work. Every rock is different and yet you look for familiar patterns. Then you meet a real challenge… Deep inside the forest plantation of Ennerdale there is a gap in the trees called the 'Pillar Ride' (see Wainwright's *The Western Fells*, Pillar 13). Half way up the ride there is a moss-covered rock. When I first came across it, I couldn't understand what had caused the 'scratch marks' across its surface. This was a fascinating forensic puzzle. "Walking poles?" – but the rock below the moss was not scratched. In fact, on close inspection, the moss simply hadn't grown over the bare strips. "Poison? Something leaching out of the rock? Copper? Iron?" – but the geology doesn't support this.

I decided to photograph the stone. It was raining heavily and the scene was so dark that without flash, I needed a five-second time exposure. Whilst setting up the camera, a raindrop landed on the rock – exactly on one of the bare patches. And that was the answer! The rock was directly below a branch of spruce and water was running down the branch and dripping off the base of the needles. Now that may or may not be exciting in itself, but consider what it takes to produce six streaks separated by just a few centimetres. The drops must land precisely on the

Deep inside the Ennerdale forest is a moss-covered rock ... but what has caused the 'scratch marks'?

same spots time after time. That means it rains here a lot but more interestingly, when it does rain – it isn't windy! If the branches were to move even just a slight amount, the pattern would not form. That's the excitement of the unexpected.

Lichens as a Diagnostic Tool

Of all the plant life encountered, I have found lichens to be the most useful when interpreting the countryside. Lichen covers almost every type of surface. It is the 'skin' of the countryside, and like skin, it can be an indicator of past conditions and underlying health.

Experienced doctors can gain valuable information by examining a patient's skin. As well as helping to diagnose specific diseases or illnesses, it can give clues as to a person's age, profession, where they have lived and what they have been in contact with. Similarly, the past history of a rock, tree or boulder can often be 'read' from the presence (or absence) of a particular lichen. The roofs of buildings at the Marchon chemical works in Whitehaven are covered in *Xanthoria parietina* – a yellow lichen that grows where there are high levels of phosphate and nitrate. For the same reason, the birdbath in your garden is surrounded by the same yellow.

You sense Sherlock Holmes ready to step in at this point:
"And then there is the curious finding of the lichen under the copper sundial."
"There *was* no lichen under the sundial."
"That was the curious finding!"

The Maps

Each map has been drawn to the largest possible scale to show the specific positions of animal signs and plant life as well as any geological and archaeological features.

When a feature is named on the map, it is referred to in the text by using bold type (e.g. **honey fungus**) to allow for easy cross-reference. An explanation of the symbols used on the maps can be found at the end of the contents section. Note in particular the symbols used for marking the gates and stiles.

Each route (except Castlerigg Stone Circle) has been marked by a line of dashes and a series of direction arrows. In most cases, the path will be obvious and well-trodden, but there may be some sections where there is no clear path to follow.

The Puzzles

On some walks, there will be a puzzle to solve. Where this occurs, the text is marked by a magnifying-glass printed in the margin. The clues may be concealed in the text or hidden within the photographs. The answers can be found in a separate 'Solutions' section at the back of the book. Don't be in a hurry to turn to this section to find the answers – a friend of mine took half a day to solve the 'Problem at Doctor Bridge', and would not have thanked me for giving him the answer in advance! You may want to cover-up the remaining solutions whilst you read the one that is immediately relevant.

Taking it Further

Most of the walks end with a section called 'Taking it Further'. This deals with certain aspects mentioned on the walk in greater detail. In some cases, a more academic approach is taken as a basis for field study projects. There are also plenty of Latin names for the would-be lichen anorak!

Equipment

In conditions when note-taking with pencil and paper is difficult (e.g., bad weather or lack of time), a Dictaphone is a useful aid. To prepare it for outdoor use, sellotape a piece of cotton wool about the size of a thimble over the microphone opening. This will eliminate the noise of the wind that would otherwise mask the recording. Don't use the Voice Activated System or you will loose the first syllables of introductory words. Try recording "parsley fern" and you will see what I mean!

Perhaps the most useful item of equipment for the 'forensic fellwalker' is a x10 hand lens. As a reasonable alternative, you could use a reversed pair of binoculars, looking through one side and holding the eye-piece close to the material being examined.

There are so many identification guides; you could be tempted to carry a small library on your back! But if I had to choose just two books, then I would include *The Wild Flowers of Britain and Northern Europe* by Richard Fitter, Alastair Fitter and Marjorie Blamey (Collins), and *The Oxford Book of Flowerless Plants* by F.H. Brightman and B.E. Nicholson (Oxford University Press). If you wish to relate your findings to the geology of the area, a geology map is essential. Choose what is called a 'Solid and Drift' edition. This shows the overlying surface materials as well as the underlying rocks.

Finally, a slow pace with frequent stops means that you won't generate as much body heat as on a normal fellwalk. It is a good idea, therefore, to pack an extra fleece jacket together with gloves and a scarf. The deerstalker hat is optional!

Bibliography

Mitchell, W.R. and Delap, P. (1974) *Lakeland Mammals*: 34. Dalesman Publications.

1. Loweswater – the Elusive Pheasant

In search of Holme Wood's best-kept secret

Checklist:

Distance: 2.5 miles.

Ascent: 460ft (140m).

Approximate Time: 1 to 2 hours.

Maps: 1:25 000 OS Explorer OL4. 1:50 000 OS Landranger 89 or 90. 1:50 000 British Geological Survey, England and Wales Sheet 29, Keswick. 1:25 000 British Geological Survey, Special Sheet NY 12, Lorton and Loweswater.

Terrain: Mostly well-defined footpaths and forest tracks that are level or with easy gradients. The descent to the 'surprise view' is narrow and partially overgrown.

Equipment and Books: Binoculars, hand lens, camera, bird and tree identification guides.

Footwear: Boots or wellingtons.

Special Considerations: Parts of this route could be closed during timber operations (not very often and for brief spells only).

Parking: Free public car park (NY122224). There is also room for 5 or 6 cars at the lay-by opposite the turn-off to Miresike (NY118225).

Public Transport: Buses from Maryport to Buttermere, Service 263 'Ennerdale Rambler' travel along the side of Loweswater to Loweswater village. Buses from Keswick to Buttermere, Stagecoach Service 77/77A 'Honister Rambler', and Cockermouth to Buttermere, Service 949 pass within 2 miles of Loweswater village.

Refreshments: Kirkstile Inn, Loweswater village.

My initial research and enquiries had indicated that I should see a pheasant in Holme Wood. This was on good authority from the National Trust who now owned the 50 hectares of mixed woodland above the south-west shore of Loweswater. I was told that it would be difficult to spot, but my best chance of seeing it was outside the wood looking across the fields from the direction of Lanthwaite Hill, or Brackenthwaite Hows as it is marked on present-day OS maps.

But I wanted to look for any signs or clues on the ground within the wood itself, for this was an important wildlife habitat in its own right. Although the area has not been designated an SSSI (Site of Special Scientific Interest), there are large numbers of mammals including red squirrels and roe deer. Recent bird surveys have recorded 35 pairs of the rare pied flycatcher, 20 pairs of wood warbler and various other species including nuthatch es, woodpeckers, owls and great crested grebe – as well as that elusive pheasant. And so, with binoculars, bird book and telephoto lens, I set off one fine September morning to investigate.

I followed the road along the north shore of Loweswater until I reached the lay-by opposite the turn-off to **Miresike**. After approximately 100 metres there is a gate and a signpost ('Public Footpath') indicating the start of the path to Holme Wood. The path leads away from the road and follows a field-drain lined with birch, ash and blackthorn. A series of footbridges and stiles takes you across the flat valley floor that was once the lake bed before the area was drained. The farmstead behind the fields to your right was named '**Waterend**' because that used to be the end of the lake.

As you cross the second set of duck-boards, there is a large area of **rush es** (*Juncus effusus*) growing in the damp ground. They mark the former lakebed. The **former shoreline** can be seen as a raised bank along the lower edge of a fertile grass pasture.

After crossing the duck-boards, the path crosses a stile to join the farm road. A stony path lined with blackberries leads down to a gate and a stile into an area of open parkland with views across Loweswater. There are a number of specimen trees all along this section. A few years ago, three oaks to the right of the path had to be removed. They were felled by a local furniture maker who shaped one of the remaining stumps into a **seat**.

Further ahead on the right of the path are two **western hemlock** (*Tsuga heterophylla*) over 30 metres high. The Latin name suggests leaves of different shape and size. The needles vary in length and have different orientations, which gives them a rather untidy appearance. The plant is not to be confused with the hemlock, *Conium maculatum*, used as a means of execution or suicide by the Greeks and Romans; nor the slower-acting water hemlock, *Cicuta virosa*, thought to have been taken by Socrates. But I am told that it makes good floorboards.

After a gate and then a small stream, the path leads straight ahead passing two magnificent **Scots pines** on the right. The path continues, passing four more Scots pines and then a cluster of tall firs known as 'grand fir' (*Abies grandis*). These can be distinguished from the hemlock by their shinier leaves, which smell of oranges.

My search now took me deep into the wood along a turn-off to the right, just opposite one of the grand firs. Care was needed here to locate this side path, which is not often used and not so obvious. This section of forest track climbs gently through an area of young beech through which can be seen more Scots pine towering up above.

Holme Force – one of Lakeland's least-visited waterfalls

Just before the track levelled out, I found a young **rowan** three metres off to the left. Its bark had been **frayed** by a roe deer. Thirty-five metres further, I reached the stone bridge that crosses Holme Beck. Here is one of Lakeland's least-visited waterfalls – **Holme Force**. To the right of the main fall on an inclined slab grows opposite-leaved golden saxifrage. But it is the non-flowering plants which catch the eye, especially around the bridge. The bridge sides have wooden guard rails and I didn't notice at first that this was in fact a stone bridge. The parapets were completely over-grown with grass and herb robert. In order to see its fine architecture, I needed to drop down carefully on the down-stream side. After negotiating the wet bank at the edge of the path, I made my way along the bridge side. The six-inch long fronds of fern growing out from between the stonework have a leathery texture with rather stiff, blackish stems, which gives it the name 'black spleenwort'.

At this point I had completely forgotten about the pheasant. Not much for the bird watcher here but plenty for the lichen hunter! My attention was drawn to a plant growing at the junction where the arch meets the ground. Here was one of the 'dog lichens'. This particular species, *Peltigera praetextata*, can be distinguished with a hand lens or reversed pair of binoculars (I knew they would come in useful!). The leaves have

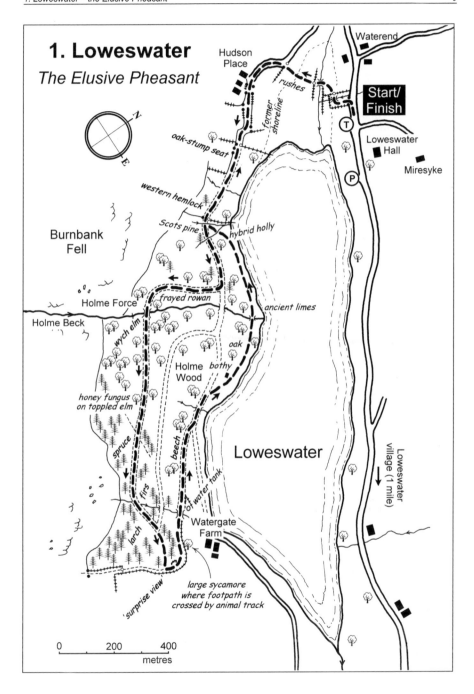

1. Loweswater
The Elusive Pheasant

Waterend

Hudson Place

rushes

Start/
Finish

former shoreline

oak-stump seat

Loweswater
Hall

Miresyke

western hemlock

Burnbank
Fell

Scots pine

hybrid holly

Holme Force

frayed rowan

ancient limes

Holme Beck

wych elm

oak

Holme
Wood

bothy

honey fungus
on toppled elm

spruce

beech

Loweswater

Loweswater
village (1 mile)

firs

larch

oil water tank

Watergate
Farm

large sycamore
where footpath is
crossed by animal track

'surprise view'

0   200   400
metres

tiny outgrowths, about the size of a pin-head, scattered over their smooth reddish brown upper surfaces.

The water level was low and so I decided to drop down and examine the underside of the bridge. Growing beneath the dripping masonry were stalactites – rods of calcium salts, formed as the mineral-rich water continuously evaporates. Underground in the still air of the Craven cave system, each drop would have its own stalagmite growing up to meet it from the floor. Outdoors, stalagmites are rare because the air is more likely to be moving, which causes the falling drops to scatter. But at the far end, under the arch, about six inches up from the ground, a five-inch stalactite had almost met up with its cone-shaped stalagmite partner. Here, the air was so still that the falling drops had been allowed to land on the same spot time and time again.

But this wasn't finding my pheasant and so I left the bridge and continued at a pace along the forest track. This section had many old **wych elm**. Three hundred metres further on from the bridge on the right was one particularly large specimen that had become infected with the **honey fungus** (*Armillaria mellea*). This is one of the most destructive fungi and here it had caused the tree to lose all its structural strength and topple over, the broken trunk coming to rest with the roots facing upwards. On careful inspection, I found a network of black filaments under the bark, which gives it the alternative name: 'bootlace fungus'. This hidden network of filaments can extend great distances. A type of honey fungus in America has recently been found with a network of bootlaces that extend almost over the whole of the forest floor, making it possibly the largest organism on the planet! In certain conditions, the infected wood will glow in the dark.

But what about the pheasant?

I was hoping to come across some evidence amongst the trees. The path up ahead looked promising as I entered an area along the back of the wood that had been densely planted with Sitka **spruce** and Douglas **fir**. The colour of the foliage changed. The path became grassy and over-grown, and quite wet in places. Significantly, a well-worn diagonal path crossed from the right and continued along a fairly straight line into the heart of the wood down to the left. I ignored the temptation of taking this easier route and continued following my path as it climbed gently through what felt like untrodden jungle. And then the path became even less distinct as it swung left, dropping down alongside a small stream. I sensed I was close to understanding the whereabouts of this pheasant as I noticed a circular area planted with **larch**, the pale yellow needles contrasting sharply with the dark green of the spruce and fir ...

The 'surprise view' from the edge of Holme Wood

Eventually I reached a junction where the forest track cut back into the heart of the wood. I wanted to reach the edge of the wood and so at this point I had to search carefully for a faint path between the trees that allowed me to continue my line of descent.

For the last mile I had been walking in what seemed like perpetual twilight when suddenly I reached the edge of the wood and everything changed. In front was a 270 degree panorama of fells. There are a number of **'surprise views'** in the Lake District but this ranks with the very best. Victorian guides would probably have named this a *coup d'oeil* if it had been on their list of 'viewing stations'. Even today, the view escapes the attention of most visitors. It is Loweswater's challenge to the experienced fellwalker: stand on this spot without a map and see if you can name the surrounding fells.

The perimeter path led back towards the lake. Down to my right across open fields I could see the buildings of **Watergate Farm**. At a point directly above the farm there was a **large sycamore** on the right of the path. I would have passed this spot if it hadn't been for a visitor up ahead, out walking his dog. On reaching the tree, the dog began sniffing frantically along the path and down by the side of the fence. I examined the ground closely and found a faint **animal track** coming out of the wood and cutting across the footpath before disappearing under the fence. There were a number of possibilities here, one of which was rabbit – but the track was too wide and there were no rabbit droppings. Another possibility was roe deer, and the track looked right – but when I examined the base of the fence, I found a gap worn away under the bottom wire. Deer would have jumped the fence. Whatever had caused this track had squeezed underneath. The gap was too small for sheep and there were no traces of wool … an interesting puzzle!

Forty metres further, on the left of the footpath, there were yet more animal tracks. On the bank sloping down to the path, half-hidden within the dry grass, were sunken hollows, some of which were connected by shallow tunnels containing piles of brown droppings. These were the tracks of a wood mouse (to be distinguished from those of a field vole, which would have left greener droppings as a result of eating mostly grass). The whole bank had been scraped and dug into, leaving the 'runs' exposed amongst patches of torn grass: the work of a hungry predator – most likely a fox.

What chance our pheasant now?

After crossing a small stream, I found a nest box on one of the large oaks to the right of the path. This was one of many nest boxes that had been placed within the wood to encourage pied flycatchers.

This bottom edge of the wood was quite different. It had been planted with **beech**, giving a rich golden colour to the wood in autumn. These beech were now becoming over-mature and, as so often happens with this species, they were infected with the bracket fungus *Ganoderma applanatum*.

After crossing a plank footbridge, a side path branched off to the right to follow the shoreline. The small **bothy** (run by the National Trust for holiday accommodation) was used originally as a fish hatchery and then as a stable for horses during timber operations.

This flat area of ground that forms the bulge in Loweswater's western shoreline is described by geologists as an 'alluvial fan'. It consists of fertile river deposits brought down by the floodwaters of Holme Beck. The old trees that grow here reflect the sheltered, fertile conditions. There were some fine **oak** and gnarled sweet chestnut and the shoreline itself was fringed with **ancient limes**. I counted over 20 specimens of lime bordering the path. Their trunks were surrounded by side-shoots, some of which were spreading out from the mother plant and self-rooting to form satellite trees.

I continued along the shoreline path. Where it turned away from the lake and just before crossing a small stream, I noticed a plant that would have been more at home in the gardens of Hampton Court: a single specimen of 'Highclere holly' (*Ilex* x *altaclerensis*) – an unusual **hybrid holly** with smooth-edged leaves. This female tree was covered in berries but for all its efforts to reproduce itself as a hybrid, the seedlings that had taken root around its base were all growing with spiky leaves, having all reverted back to the original form.

I continued following the path until it reached the main forest track and from here retraced my route back to the car. I drove along the narrow shoreline road towards Loweswater village with my sights set on a bar meal at the Kirkstile Inn. It had been a magnificent walk through one of Lakeland's least-known woodlands – the equal of any in Borrowdale. All that remained was to get a photograph of the pheasant. I had been told that my best chance of spotting it was here, along the roadside, looking back across the fields in the direction of the lake. I stopped the car in a driveway, but I was too late. The light had gone.

It wasn't until later in the year that I received an E-mail from a friend who had just visited the wood.

"I thought you might like to see this – taken around 10am on the 5th December looking across Loweswater."

I opened the attachment and watched the digital image appear on the screen. And there it was – the pheasant – a beautiful mosaic of colour, its yellow eye looking back at me across the fields!

 Look carefully at the photograph. The pheasant is there but it is difficult to spot. If you still cannot find it, turn to the 'Solutions' section at the back of the book.

Spot the pheasant (© Howard Holden 2003)

Taking it Further

Loweswater is shrinking as it fills up with silt and organic debris. It is described as a *eutrophic* lake (from the Greek *eu* meaning 'well', and *trophic* meaning 'feed'). The feeding effect comes from the fertiliser applied to the surrounding farmland and the run-off of organically rich soils. A consequence of this is the rapid growth of the diatom *Asterionella*, which produces an 'algal bloom' in summer. As it decays, the oxygen level in the water is used up and toxins are produced.

Loweswater provides an example of what botanists call a 'hydroseral climax', where plant-cover begins with low-lying vegetation such as reeds and rushes, to be finally succeeded by scrub and woodland (see Bellamy 1985).

Bibliography

Bellamy, D. (1985) *Exploring the British Countryside*: 144 –157. Newnes Books.

2. Buttermere – the Problem of the Missing Ramp

A lakeside walk recalling preparations for D-Day

Checklist:

Distance: 4.3 miles.

Ascent: Negligible.

Approximate Time: 2½ hours.

Maps: 1:25 000 OS Explorer OL4.
1:50 000 OS Landranger 89 or 90.
1:50 000 British Geological Survey,
England and Wales Sheet 29, Keswick.

Terrain: Fairly level paths plus a section of roadside walking from Gatesgarth to Hassness.

Equipment and Books: Wild flower and tree guide, hand lens.

Footwear: Boots or wellingtons.

Special Considerations: A good walk for a wet day.

Parking: Public car park, Buttermere (NY174169).

Public Transport: Buses from Keswick to Buttermere, Stagecoach Service 77/77A 'Honister Rambler'; Maryport to Buttermere, Service 263 'Ennerdale Rambler'; Cockermouth to Buttermere, Service 949.

Refreshments: The Fish Hotel and the Bridge Hotel in Buttermere.

My friend Howard is a keen photographer. "Ever seen a photograph of the concrete ramp at Buttermere?" I asked him over the telephone.

"What ramp?"

"The one used by the Army to drive their trucks and jeeps into the lake in preparation for D-Day. I read about it sometime ago in Wainwright – he mentioned them at the Sourmilk Gill end. I can't remember where in Wainwright I saw it but I checked in a book by Millward and Robinson, and an aerial shot taken in the early-70s shows what could be a rectangular structure jutting into the water. But the resolution wasn't clear enough to make it out."

We discussed it some more and he said he would look through a few of his old photographs and get back to me later. In the meantime, I decided to look over the area for myself to see if there were any clues remaining. It was 60 years since the ramp was last used but concrete structures large enough to carry army vehicles would surely not disappear completely.

I set off following the farm lanes from outside the Fish Hotel to where the National Trust keep their caravan. I took the direct path to the water's edge. This was the area in which it was all supposed to have happened.

The path skirted the lake alongside a line of oak trees. At the top of the

The slipway between the last two oak trees ... but not a trace of the ramp could be found.

shoreline, a low wall had recently been constructed marking the edge of the grass field. The top of the wall was held firm with patches of concrete. The trouble was, everywhere had been tidied up. You couldn't tell if the bits of concrete on the shore were from the ramp or had fallen out of the wall. I found an old piece of rusty iron chain in the water, about a foot long and badly corroded – could *this* be significant?

The problem was the soft water. Any small pieces of submerged concrete would start to dissolve away – and it was over 60 years ago. The last two oak trees in the line straddled what appeared to be a natural slipway down to the water, but not a trace of the ramp could be found.

I took some photographs and moved on, crossing two footbridges and a gate to join the main path along Buttermere's south-west shoreline. The trees along this section are quite magnificent with some extremely fine specimens of sycamore, Scots pine and sweet chestnut. On the right of the path I passed a particularly large specimen of the bracket fungus *Polyporus* growing out from the base of a sweet chestnut.

After passing through a gap in a wall and crossing a stream, I entered an area of larch. A fenced-off enclosure to the right of the path had been **clear-felled** as an experiment in forest regeneration – to see how the natural vegetation develops when sheep are kept out. After approximately 200 metres, I stopped alongside two sawn-off tree stumps just left

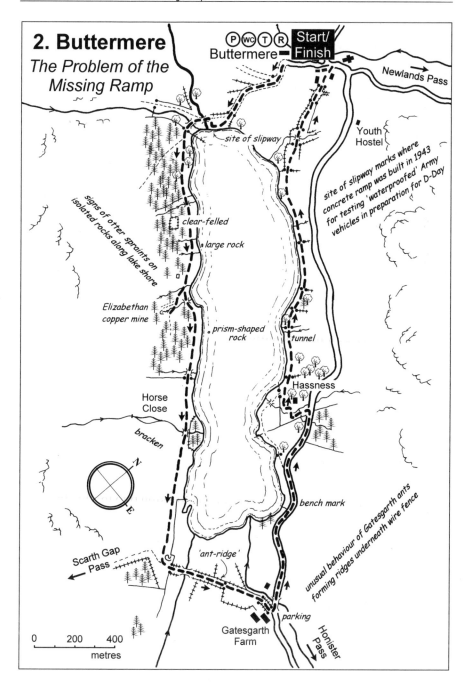

2. Buttermere
The Problem of the Missing Ramp

Ⓟ ⓦⓒ Ⓣ Ⓡ **Start/Finish**
Buttermere

Newlands Pass

site of slipway

Youth Hostel

site of slipway marks where concrete ramp was built in 1943 for testing 'waterproofed' Army vehicles in preparation for D-Day

signs of otter spraints on isolated rocks along lake shore

clear-felled

large rock

Elizabethan copper mine

prism-shaped rock

tunnel

Hassness

Horse Close

bracken

bench mark

N

E

unusual behaviour of Gatesgarth ants forming ridges underneath wire fence

Scarth Gap Pass

'ant-ridge'

parking

Gatesgarth Farm

Honister Pass

0   200   400
metres

of the path. From here I could see a **large rock** projecting from the water, just out from the shoreline. (The situation will vary depending on the height of the lake, and after very heavy rain the top of this rock may be submerged.) I carefully dropped down to the lake edge to take a closer look. On the top of the rock I found some small bones. Through the hand lens I spotted grey fragments ranging in size from one to ten millimetres amongst which was a complete vertebra with concave discs at each end. This is the diagnostic shape of fish vertebrae and there was only one animal that would have left this here – an otter! This must be one of the busiest paths in the Lake District and yet just metres away were signs of otter. Fortunately, the water level had been low for a number of weeks and there had been little wind to whip up any swell, otherwise this evidence would have been washed away.

Otter droppings or 'spraints' are likely to be found on prominent land-marks, the same spot being used quite regularly. The pale-coloured top of this rock was the colour of the bare rock, but immediately below was a band of green moss and algae. When conditions within an environment change gradually along a gradient, plants tend to occupy distinct posi-tions or 'zones'. On the top of this rock, the phosphates and nitrates from the digested fish are so concentrated that nothing grows. At a certain distance out, the concentration is at an optimum for growth; further out still and the fertilising effect disappears. What is significant here is that this rock is washed by wave-action, and the moss and algae can only grow if the gradient of chemicals is constantly being renewed.

I returned to the path and continued on my route. The shoreline up ahead had become incut to form a shallow bay filled with shingle and small stones. A sudden change in the outline of a lake often reflects a change in the geology. The geology map showed that a narrow band of granite had intruded into the surrounding Skiddaw Group rocks at this point on the shore. The junction was marked by a vein of copper.

Above the inlet, the path crosses a narrow stream flowing out from the spruce plantation. The path then rises over a mound of fine gravel that is in fact the spoil heap of an **Elizabethan copper mine**. At this point, the main path continues through the forest whilst a side path branches off left to follow the shoreline. The old mine can be found by continuing a few metres along the main track to where a second stream emerges from the sloping ground up to the right. The entrance or adit can be found at the back of a horseshoe-shaped ridge of earth, but the opening is now blocked-off with large granite boulders.

I retraced my steps back to the path junction and followed the narrow stony track, crossing the adit stream by a wooden footbridge. The band of underlying granite had restricted the drainage of the surface soil just off to the right of the path. The result was a waterlogged area of peat with a wonderful array of wetland plants – jointed rush and star sedge together with bog asphodel and various orchids.

I followed the path over a rock outcrop that jutted out from the shore-line. Several metres further, a spring emerged below the path. The permanently wet ground was covered with the pale green star-fish-shaped leaves of butterwort. Ten metres further along from the spring, I noticed a **prism-shaped rock** standing proud of the water just out from the lake edge. The sloping, flat surface that faced out into the lake was covered in yellow lichen. This is the classic sign of a surface that has been used as a bird perch, in this case, by shoreline birds such as dippers and wagtails. Further examination with a hand lens revealed the tell-tale grey fragments of fish bone. Here was another rock used by otters.

Biologists place otters within a family group known as the mustelids of which skunks are also members. Scent plays a major part in their communication and if the otter spraints are fresh, they will have a distinctive aroma!

I rejoined the path, crossed a footbridge and then passed through a gate in a wall. The fellside opened out over slopes of bracken with views to the right of High Crag. On the map, the area named Horse Close is char-acterised by a series of cascading waterfalls. The west side of the Buttermere valley has many waterfalls between the 150 and 200 metre contour line: a sign of the extra deepening of the valley by late glacial action. Warnscale Beck, Sourmilk Gill, Far Ruddy Beck and Scale Force are all worth a visit, but the volume of water rushing down into Horse Close is exceptional and remains almost constant even during a dry spell. The loose material carried down has produced a large bulge in the shoreline – a fertile delta, now planted with larch.

 The shoreline now becomes a marshy flat on which grows the occasional oak. After passing a sheep-fold, the path bears left over a footbridge and then closely follows the straight line of a wire fence. There was something different about this fence. The eight strands of rusty wire were much thicker than those found on modern fences, which suggested that it was unusually old. Underneath the bottom wire, the ground was raised up to form a ridge. The grass looked especially healthy and the soil, where it was exposed, had a sandy texture. I poked the area with my stick, and out came a party of ants! Here were the usual Lakeland ants (the yellow meadow ant) but not the usual dome-shaped ant-hills. It would seem that these Buttermere ants had migrated under the line of fence wire to form an almost continuous ant-hill, or more accurately – an **'ant-ridge'**. Why? [see 'Solutions' section for an explanation]

I continued following the path to Gatesgarth Farm and joined the road in the direction of Buttermere village. The much-photographed Scots pines that grow along the shingle strand-line now came into view on the left. Soon after passing the wall that cuts across in the direction of the pines, I noticed something strange on the roadside footpath. An arrow had been neatly carved into the surface of a smooth rock. For a moment I wondered if this could be the stylised 'crow's foot' arrow used by the Ministry of Defence. I suddenly remembered the concrete ramps. Could this be evidence that the Army had been in Buttermere? But it was all wishful thinking – on studying the old 1:10 000 OS map, the arrow proved to be nothing more than an Ordnance Survey **bench mark**!

Two alternatives were now available. I could follow the lower shoreline path that leads away from the road down to the left, or I could keep to the road for a quarter of a mile and join the footpath that drops down to the lake through the oak and beech woods of Hassness. The road was quiet and so I decided on the latter.

The path through the wood crosses two footbridges. It then follows a wall, notable for its fine covering of the 'green' algae, *Trentepholia*, which here has developed a bright orange pigment in response to sunlight – and so does not appear green at all!

After reaching the shoreline, I passed through a gate in some iron railings. There

The bench mark on the roadside path

were some particularly fine patches of bell heather (*Erica cinerea*) growing high up on the right, with the more typical *Calluna vulgaris* below. The light-level dropped as I entered a section of beech wood. To the right of the path, an oak was growing on a flat boulder. At an early stage, its roots had found their way into a number of cracks. Now that the roots had expanded, the rock had been split open.

Once through the famous rock **tunnel** and then through a gate, I noticed a young maple in an open grassy area on the right. On this September evening its leaves were turning gold and scarlet. The path now crossed a delightful area of parkland with a variety of unusual trees – a strangely-contorted larch, another larch growing completely horizontal, and a fine specimen of sweet chestnut developing a slight spiral in its trunk. There was also a number of old wych elms and limes, which appeared surprisingly normal!

This was a glorious end to the walk. But the ramp had eluded me. Some days later however, I received a telephone call:

"Hello! Howard here – I think I've found the ramp!"

Several phone calls later – I had the evidence in my hand – a film taken in 1943 showing the preparations for D-Day: a 15 cwt truck driving down the ramp into the lake, driving with wheels still in contact with the lake bed and almost submerged. These vehicles were specially prepared by the Army's Driving and Maintenance School based at Keswick. Extensive training was carried out following a prescribed circuit at the north end of the lake, navigating around a fixed marker buoy before returning to the shore.

It's all history now. Almost forgotten. The ramp has gone. The small hut with the corrugated iron roof (used for changing out of wet clothes) has been cleared away.

But the oak trees still mark the **site of the slip-way**, and the unmistak-

Going … going … gone! A specially waterproofed 15 cwt Bedford truck is tested in Buttermere in preparation for the 1944 D-Day landings.

able profile of Fleetwith Pike shows that it actually happened – here at Buttermere!

Taking it Further

The behaviour of the Gatesgarth ants is similar to a population of red wood ants in an area of limestone pavement near Silverdale. Here, some very old colonies were found underneath bramble thickets and not in their usual position in open grassland. The Silverdale colonies were surrounded by grazing cattle and it would seem that they had escaped being trampled by migrating to a safer position (Robinson 2003).

But is this really 'learnt' behaviour? Are the Buttermere ants actively building along the line of the wire, or is it more a passive result of a few fortunate colonies being left in the one safe place and over time merging to form a ridge?

If it is active learning, how long has it taken to become established? There are records of a dairy farm, or *vaccary*, at Gatesgarth since 1280 (see Rollinson 1988). It would be interesting to know if this ant behaviour is dependent on a long and continuous period of cattle grazing. To what extent is it found in areas where cattle have only recently been introduced?

The effect may also be caused by mechanical cultivation. It is quite noticeable how the flat fields that border the lake have eroded to a lower level than the field edges: evidence of a long history of ploughing and harrowing.

Bibliography

Robinson, N.A. (2003) Wood ants at Coldwell Parrock, '_Keer to Kent_' **50:** 7-8.

Rollinson, W. (1988) _The Lake District: Landscape Heritage_: 80. David and Charles.

3. Newlands Valley – the Witch's Hand

Uncovering Barrow's mining legacy

Checklist:

Distance: 4 miles.

Ascent: 1080ft (330m).

Approximate Time: 2½ hours.

Maps: 1:25 000 OS Explorer OL4.
1:50 000 OS Landranger 89 or 90.
1:50 000 British Geological Survey,
England and Wales Sheet 29, Keswick.

Terrain: Easy gradients on good roads or paths except for brief sections involving some steep grass banks in Stoneycroft Gill.

Equipment: Hand lens and camera.

Footwear: Boots.

Special Considerations: After heavy rain, the paths alongside Stoneycroft Gill may be flooded.

Parking: Roadside space for up to 12 cars opposite Uzzicar Farm (NY233218).

Public Transport: Buses from Keswick to Cockermouth. Stagecoach Service X5, stops at Braithwaite.

Refreshments: The Swinside Inn provides excellent bar meals as well as one of the best views across the valley of 'the witch's hand'.

My first visit to Barrow was just after the fire. It was the First of May 2003 and you could still smell the burnt heather stalks. A week earlier, the whole fell side had been swept by flames that had jumped across onto Stile End and even parts of Outerside. Now it was six months later, and I wanted to see how things had changed.

I parked the car on the broad roadside parking space opposite **Uzzicar** and set off down the road to the bridge at **Stoneycroft**. I took a narrow path through the encroaching gorse, starting next to the bridge, and followed the north bank of Stoneycroft Gill. The reason for choosing this prickly route was to follow a trench that had been cut through the rock to divert the flow from the stream bed. This was the site of the ancient Stoneycroft Mine. An accident here in 1690 had resulted in miners being trapped when the dam diverting the water had failed. The mine was reopened in 1846 but the bodies were never found (see Adams 1995).

The path kept crossing and running alongside the rock trench until it reached the mine road. Here, at a point marked by a **manhole** cover, a narrow path cut back down towards the gill. A group of youngsters and their instructors from the nearby Activity Centre were just returning from a session of gorge scrambling. I crossed over to a path that followed the south side of the gill. This was a delightful section. The water had cut a series of smooth channels through the rock – a kind of bobsleigh-run through water.

The bank was lined with holly, birch and oak. After nearly 200 metres, I reached one of the mine entrances –a deep **adit** fringed with rowan and ferns. I crossed back to the other side and climbed the steep grassy bank. I joined a path that led past a hidden quarry face. In front of this secret spot, the path became a concrete strip encasing an iron pipe complete with **stop valve**. I followed the pipe to its source – a concrete collection chamber. Here was yet more engineering aimed at diverting the flow of water away from the mines. I climbed back up the grassy bank toward the mine road and crossed a third device for redirecting the water

– a shallow **'leat'** leading away from the gill from where there had once been a **dam**.

One hundred metres after joining the road, I came to a left junction. It led to a level area with a small mound of **overgrown spoil**. The only plant that seemed to be colonising its loose, toxic surface was a moss, *Polytrichun urnigerum* – a 'pioneer species' of acid soil that was thriving from the lack of competition.

I climbed across the grass to rejoin the quarry road. In April, the fire had swept along this valley driven by an east wind. The road had acted as a fire-break and all the damage was kept to its northern side. After the fire, the area above the

Looking down Stoneycroft Gill two days after the April 2003 fire. Notice how the mine road acted as a fire break.

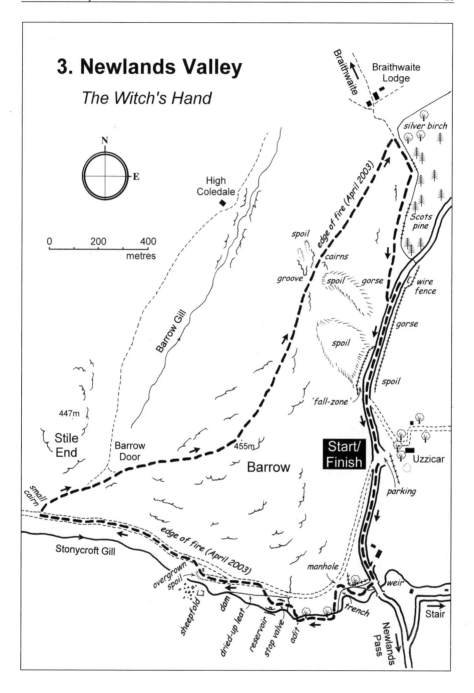

3. Newlands Valley

The Witch's Hand

Braithwaite

Braithwaite
Lodge

silver birch

Scots
pine

High
Coledale

N

E

0   200   400
metres

spoil

edge of fire (April 2003)

cairns

groove

spoil

gorse

wire
fence

gorse

Barrow Gill

spoil

spoil

'fall-zone'

447m

Stile
End

Barrow
Door

455m

Barrow

Start/
Finish

Uzzicar

small
cairn

parking

edge of fire (April 2003)

Stonycroft Gill

manhole

weir

overgrown
spoil

sheepfold

dam

dried-up leat

reservoir

stop valve

adit

french

Newlands
Pass

Stair

road was black. Now the bracken had grown back, although in much thinner stands. Underneath the scattered stems were the first signs of heather: tiny shoots just a few centimetres long, most of which were bell heather (*Erica cinerea*). Tormentil was putting out its yellow flowers as if nothing had happened.

After approximately 700 metres, a **small cairn** at the side of the road signalled the start of a narrow path that climbed across the south-west flank of Barrow. At times, the path was so narrow, it resembled a sheep track, but it finally led me to the rocky col of **Barrow Door**. Before April, these rocks had a covering of crottle. Now they were burnt clean by the heat that must have been at its most intense along the ridge. Before the fire, the heather would have supported a mixture of cup lichens and 'reindeer lichens'. Six months later there appeared to be only black ash.

I reached the top of Barrow with the sun streaking through the clouds above Causey Pike. These north-west ridges always seem to be at their best in the early evening light. The views over Keswick to Skiddaw opened out as I followed the ridge down to the stony outcrop that marked another lead mine. The **spoil**-heaps had formed narrow ridges on the Coledale side. Most of the ore seems to have been won near the surface, leaving trough-shaped gullies and **grooves** on the west side of the ridge.

Evening sunlight over Causey Pike from the summit ridge on Barrow

Barrow is recognised by its massive spoil-heaps that face the Newlands Valley. A bird's-eye view of these was just visible on peering over the east side of the ridge. But nothing from this angle gave away their extent or indicated why they had been called 'the witch's hand'.

The path now led down a grass strip with bracken on either side. Such wide grass strips amongst the bracken are a feature of these lower slopes, indicating just how effective we are with our trampling feet in keeping the bracken at bay. At the bottom of this grassy highway, I turned right to follow a delightful, sheltered path along the side of a plantation of birch and Scots pine. On reaching the road, I took a short detour to the left for 100 metres to examine the fence in front of a roadside seat. So far, this walk had been a classic half-day fell walk with attention focused on the expansive views. That was about to change. This last section was all about those mundane objects that are simply passed by – the fenceposts!

The **wire fence** that bordered the road was the scene of an ecological whodunnit, but to appreciate what was happening here, I had to be in the right frame of mind … In the play *Night must Fall* by Emlyn Williams, there is a moment when you suddenly realise that the main character has the victim's head concealed in a hat-box. That moment of discovery happens only once, and can never shock the same way again – however many times you see the play. The same happens when you approach a fencepost and discover for the first time what is causing the lichen to grow in such a strange pattern. It is the process of teasing-out the answer that builds-up the excitement, finally arriving at that one moment when you realise what is happening. You could call it 'the hat-box effect'.

The pattern that I was about to see is only fleetingly seen in the Lake District (it is seen at its best in parts of the western Highlands and Islands of Scotland). I selected one of the posts and looked closely at the lichens. They were growing in a narrow band, two inches down from the top. In some places, it looked as if someone had scraped the surface clean with a ruler. What was happening here?

To solve the puzzle, you could list all the ecological factors – all the usual suspects: sunlight, wind direction, the cross-grain of the wood holding moisture, birds landing on top, sheep rubbing lower down, sulphur dioxide from passing cars, fire – as happened in April… but still the culprit would go unseen. So far, the question had been: "Why was the lichen growing in this uneven pattern?" The answer began to emerge only when the question changed: "What was stopping the lichen from covering the whole surface?"

The route back along the road provided yet further studies of fenceposts set amongst the encroaching gorse. Eventually I reached the

The fencepost mystery. The pattern of lichens on a simple fencepost becomes a complex ecological study. Lichen growth is affected by the direction of the sun and wind, the grain of the wood, birds perching, sheep rubbing, pollution from cars, and fire. But one effect is dominant above all the others ...[see Solutions].

foot of the main spoil-heap from the Barrow lead mines. This is thought to be the largest man-made scree slope in the Lake District, but the effect is not all man-made. The scar has failed to heal due in part to the toxic effects of the lead, but there is also the constant movement of fine rock particles. The geology map shows Barrow to be composed of Skiddaw Group rock cut through on the Newlands side by a vein of lead and zinc. But there is also a horizontal layer of what geologists call 'greywacke sandstone'. It is this extensive layer of unstable, sandy material that has destabilised the whole of Barrow's eastern side. The mining activity had disturbed a Balrog! The history of the Barrow Mine is one plagued by problems of shafts being filled and blocked by the fine particles of quartz and sand. It has also been an ongoing problem for the County Roads Department. A **'fall-zone'** was dug away on the up-slope side of the road to allow space for material slipping down. But the over-steepened lower slope remains a problem, and 'the witch's hand' continues to move.

Taking it Further

Since the fire in April 2003, Barrow has become an interesting site for studying the process of plant colonisation and succession. The succession of lichens following heather burning has been closely studied on other moorland sites (see Coppins and Shimwell 1971, quoted in Gilbert 2000). Four phases have been identified during the course of regeneration after a fire:

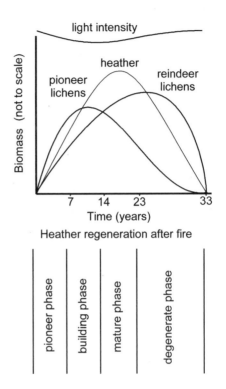

Figure 3.1 The sequence of regeneration and recolonisation of a heather moorland after fire (adapted from Coppins and Shimwell 1971).

❖ A 'pioneer phase' in which the peat surface is colonised by the browny black crusts of *Placynthiella* followed by the 'cup lichen' – *Cladonia coccifera* and the 'matchstick lichen' – *C. floerkeana.*

❖ A 'building phase' in which the young heather shelters a wider range of *Cladonia* species including the 'cup lichens' – *C. chlorophaea, C. crispata, C. fimbriata, C. macilenta, C. ramulosa.*

❖ A 'mature phase' in which the heather is at its most dense, and the reduction in light causes a drop in lichen numbers.

❖ A 'degenerate phase' in which the heather declines with age, and the dying stems let in more light for colonisation by the 'reindeer lichens' – *Cladonia uncialis* and *C. arbuscula.*

The whole cycle will repeat itself after approximately 33 years (the average lifespan of heather), or earlier if the moor is once again cleared by fire (see Figure 3.1).

Bibliography

Adams, J. (1995) *Mines of the Lake District Fells*, 2nd edition: 39-43. Dalesman Publications.

Coppins, B.J and Shimwell, D.W. (1971) Cryptogam complement and biomass in dry *Calluna* heaths of different ages, *Oikos* **22**: 204-209.

Gilbert, O.L. (2000) *Lichens*: 118-130. The New Naturalist Library, HarperCollins.

4. Castlerigg Stone Circle – the Cadbury Connection

Five experts go on a treasure hunt

Checklist:

Distance: Negligible.

Ascent: Negligible.

Approximate Time: Allow 1hour.

Maps: 1:25 000 OS Explorer OL4. 1:50 000 OS Landranger 90.

Terrain: Level, grassy field.

Equipment: Camera, hand lens.

Footwear: Leather sandals.

Special Considerations: The circle is a Scheduled Ancient Monument. It is an offence to disturb or deface it or to use a metal detector within a 33ft/10m boundary of any of the features. Please avoid climbing or sitting on the stones.

Parking: Ample parking space opposite northern entrance (NY292237).

Public Transport: Walking distance from Keswick bus station is 2miles. Stagecoach Service 73/73A (Keswick to Carlisle) stops at the stone circle.

Refreshments: Keswick.

The following case is based on documentary evidence. The meeting and characters, however, are entirely imaginary ...

Scene: south-west entrance to the Castlerigg field.

Characters in order of appearance:

ARCHAEO – an archaeologist

GEO – a geophysicist

SKEPTICO – a doubter

AQUARIUS – a follower of 'New Age' philosophies

LICHEO – a lichenologist

It took five of us to work out what 'Cadbury' had to do with it. We were in Keswick and had agreed to meet at the Stone Circle. Archaeo had been told to look out for the Cadbury Hole but none of us had any idea what a 'Cadbury' hole might be ...

ARCHAEO: "This is the best place to start. Here we can see an outlying stone hidden in the boundary wall. Almost everyone misses this. Once you are inside the field, the stone cannot be seen."

From the road, we all peered across to the south-facing side of the southern boundary wall. At a point approximately one and a half metres in from the road, we could see the **hidden outlier** built into the wall base. We crossed the stone stile and immediately came across a **second outlier**, one metre north-east of the stile. The scratch marks on this stone were once thought to be an ancient form of writing called Ogham Script,

Castlerigg Stone Circle

but they are now accepted as plough marks. The stone circle was in the centre of a grassy field with few surface features outside the ring of stones. There was, however, evidence of medieval cultivation strips known to archaeologists as **'rig and furrow'** that extended around the northern edge. There was also an area of uneven ground outside the south-west edge of the circle.

ARCHAEO: [turning to one of his colleagues]: "Did the geophysical survey show anything of interest?"

GEO: "Not much, I'm afraid, except for an area of confused readings outside the south-west quadrant of the circle – possibly indicating some buried stones."

ARCHAEO: "No sign of the third outlier mentioned by Morrow in 1907? It's supposed to lie at a point 200 metres south-west from the centre. Anderson couldn't find it in 1914. He thought the top of the stone had broken off. It shows how things change over the years ... If we look at Dymond's 1877 plan, he indicates that stones 13, 14 and 15 had possibly been moved even as far back as then."

SKEPTICO: "Now wait a minute. I have the map drawn by Anderson and he refers to these same stones as 26, 25 and 24, as do the plans in the

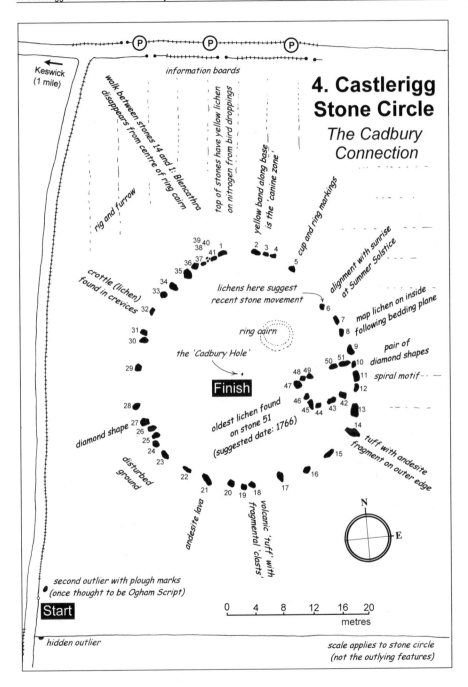

Keswick
(1 mile)

information boards

walk between stones 14 and 1: Blencathra disappears from centre of ring cairn

rig and furrow

4. Castlerigg Stone Circle
The Cadbury Connection

top of stones have yellow lichen on nitrogen from bird droppings

yellow band along base is the 'canine zone'

cup and ring markings

alignment with sunrise at Summer Solstice

crottle (lichen) found in crevices

lichens here suggest recent stone movement

map lichen on inside following bedding plane

ring cairn

pair of diamond shapes

the 'Cadbury Hole'

spiral motif

Finish

oldest lichen found on stone 51 (suggested date: 1766)

diamond shape

tuff with andesite fragment on outer edge

disturbed ground

andesite lava

volcanic 'tuff' with fragmental 'clasts'

N
E

second outlier with plough marks
(once thought to be Ogham Script)

Start

0   4   8   12   16   20
metres

hidden outlier

scale applies to stone circle
(not the outlying features)

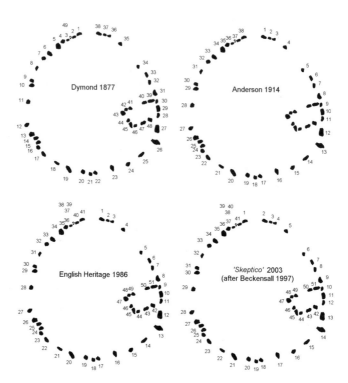

Figure 4.1 'The Magic Circle' – each time you count the stones, the numbers change!

English Heritage survey. But Beckensall's 1997 report has them numbered 27, 26, and 25."

AQUARIUS: "That's hardly surprising. There is a tradition that you cannot count the number of stones in a stone circle – the numbers change each time you try!"

SKEPTICO: "That's ridiculous. We live in a scientific age and we can't even count and label 41 objects in a circle?"

ARCHAEO: "Well, it depends where you start counting and whether you go round clockwise or counter-clockwise."

SKEPTICO: "Astonishing! – We have 300 years of serious academic study beginning with Stukely in 1725 and leading to Beckensall in 2002, and we still can't be sure which is stone 27 or any of the other stones for that matter. There seems to be no universally accepted numbering system!

"Imagine in Genetics: '...well, we're not sure whether this is chromosome 26 or 27.' And: '...we are just about to sequence the DNA, but we may start counting the bases from this end, or there again, maybe the other – and we may miss a few out if they don't show up clearly.'

"Back problems would be a nightmare: '7th thoracic vertebra, or was that the 28th?' And don't even think of having surgery on your fingers.

"We may as well stop right now if we can't agree on a numbering system."

ARCHAEO: "Well, the convention usually adopted is to label the entrance stones: 1 and 2, and then go round in a clockwise direction. So I think we should standardise all our drawings accordingly."

Everyone was in agreement and we were able to start at stone 1...

GEO: "Volcanic tuff – smooth surface indicating an erratic of the Borrowdale Volcanic Group transported here by ice, probably from Thirlmere – typical of most of these stones."

LICHEO: "Notice the **yellow lichen** on top, probably *Candelariella vitellina* – indicating a bird-perching site. And also the band of yellow around its base – this is one of the first stones to be visited and is a favourite stopping place for visitors' dogs."

ARCHAEO: "OK. Stone 2 – and it looks more or less the same... as do 3 and 4. According to Beckensall, stone 5 is supposed to have **cup and ring markings** on the top. You can just make-out a fraction of the ring but the top section is missing. Now we have a gap and we are at stone 6..."

AQUARIUS: "This is a significant stone. Anderson's 1914 plan summarises the findings of Morrow and Thom and shows the top of this stone to form an **alignment with the sunrise** at the Summer Solstice."

SKEPTICO: "But that could be pure coincidence – they have to line up somewhere. And what if the stone has been moved since the circle was built?"

ARCHAEO: "There is evidence that this has happened. Hutchinson's *History of Cumberland* in 1794-97 has an illustration showing that stones 6 to 10 were all lying flat on the ground. And then Otley's 1848-49 plan shows them repositioned, upright – as we see them now."

SKEPTICO *[with tongue in cheek]*: "I have a theory that all the stones were initially arranged on their sides, for sitting on, and then archaeologists came along and stood them all upright!"

ARCHAEO: "Except that a report by Gray as early as 1769 describes 'most of them still erect'."

LICHEO: "The problem is that stone 6 has been moved quite recently! The top would have been leaning over to the north by about a quarter of a metre. Look at the base on the north side. There is a diagonal line running down into the ground that used to be the soil level. It has been repositioned and the surface that was once below ground-level has been exposed. The lichens that colonised this fresh area are much smaller in size – no more than 30 years old.

ARCHAEO: "OK. Let's move on now to stones 10 and 11 because these have caused quite a stir recently. Number 10 has a **pair of diamond shapes** and number 11 a **spiral motif** on its inner side. This was reported by Beckensall in 1997 and thought to be an example of prehistoric rock art. A similar spiral has been found at Long Meg. *[A party of tourists arrives.]*

"It's getting quite busy just here. Everyone seems to converge on stones 13 and 14 for some reason. I suppose 13 acts as a seat alongside the largest stone in the circle. Let's move on to examine the south-west quadrant. A number of these stones have been moved, and an interesting **diamond shape** has been carved on stone 27 – described by Beckensall as another possible example of prehistoric rock art."

SKEPTICO: "But do we know the date? It may be modern graffiti."

ARCHAEO: "That's a fair point. There are lots of documented examples of how the stones were abused". Coleridge, for example, tell us that "the Keswickians have been playing Tricks with the stones". He recalls that the "white-vested Wizards" had been white-washed! And there are many accounts recalling how the increase in tourism during the late 1800s and early 1900s led to an increase in vandalism with people carving their initials on many of the stones."

LICHEO: "There was a period soon after 1913, when the National Trust bought the site, and the stones were thoroughly cleaned. Almost all of the oldest lichens can be traced back to this event. As well as the use of bleach and weedkiller, it is possible that the stone surfaces were actually ground smooth to remove the graffiti."

SKEPTICO: "And so these rock art features may be prehistoric in origin, or Victorian graffiti that the National Trust didn't quite manage to remove?"

LICHEO: "It's impossible to say one way or the other."

Our group continued along the north-west quadrant. There was nothing much to note except the gap between stones 37 and 41 with a group of

Which one is Skeptico?

three stones only a few inches high (one of the places where the numbering goes astray). Having completed our circuit without once mentioning the Cadbury Hole, we headed across to examine the inner rectangle.

ARCHAEO: "No one knows the purpose of the rectangle but it's what makes Castlerigg unique. The documentary evidence points to it being contemporaneous with the outer ring. Stukely, for instance, mentions it as early as 1725."

SKEPTICO: "But the circle is thought to date from the early Bronze Age – that's 3000 BC!"

ARCHAEO: "That's a fair point. But then all our information fails to go back as far as we would like. I think the rectangle shares a similar history to the outer circle – it certainly has suffered similar stone movements! Look at stone 47 for instance. In 1848, Otley showed it to be in line with the rest of the rectangle. Now it lies one metre out of position to the north-west."

LICHEO: "Before leaving the rectangle, I think we ought to look at stone 51. Winchester found the **oldest lichen** here, at the base of the south-facing side. The diameter of the lichen fragment suggested a date of 1766."

AQUARIUS: "Stone 51 is also thought to have the faint outline of a circle or the outer part of a spiral carved on the same inner surface."

ARCHAEO: " I'm keeping an eye on the clock … and we have still to find the 'Cadbury Hole'. Before lunch, I think we ought to examine the so-called ring cairns or ring ditches. The one in the north-west quadrant is barely visible unless the light is low. The other we can just about make-out in the north-east quadrant."

AQUARIUS: "There is a suggestion that this predates the circle. From the position of the **ring cairn**, the profile of certain stones appears to match or 'echo' the outline of the distant fells. Also, if you walk the bearing between Helvellyn and Skiddaw, along the line connecting stone 14 and stone 1, and at the same time watch Blencathra – the moment Blencathra disappears behind Gategill Fell, you find that you are in the centre of the ring! There could be many cross-reference points inside the stone circle that could pinpoint a secret burial site or the location of a relic or treasure."

 ARCHAEO: "That reminds me … here is **the 'Cadbury Hole'** that we've all been looking for – right in the centre of the Circle – a small disturbed area about 0.3 metres in diameter. And while we all consider again: "Why *Cadbury*?"… I think it's time for something to eat!" [See 'Solutions' if you would like to know what happened here.]

Taking it Further

One of the best photographs showing the surface features of the site can be found in Warren and Sasitorn (2003). They show an aerial photograph of the field with a light dusting of snow and low evening light. Outside the circle, the rig and furrow marks are remarkably well depicted, whilst inside the circle, *three* ring ditches can be clearly seen occupying the north-east, north-west and south-west quadrants respectively.

Care should be taken, however, when interpreting the surface features inside the circle. The ring ditches may be Bronze Age features but it has been suggested that they are artefacts, left behind after the removal of tree roots. In support of this, early nineteenth century illustrations show the circle to be set amongst trees with a group of tall conifers inside the circle. A report from this period states that '…within this magical circle, a small plantation of larch trees environ part of the stones…' (see Horne,1816; Allom,1836; and Pyne,1859 quoted in Fraser *et al.*, 1986).

The Castlerigg site is an unexpected source of information for the student of ecology and animal behaviour. The key is the distribution of lichens (see Figure 4.2). When analysing these distribution patterns it is

Stone	Height (metres)	Geology (all volcanic erratics)	Surface Features (N = north, E = east, S = south, W = west)
1	1.73	tuff (volcanic ash)	bird perch, canine zone on S side
2	1.68	tuff, vertical bedded	bird perch, canine zone on S side
3	0.97	tuff, angular clasts	smooth top, climbed on
4	0.97	tuff	canine zone on SE side
5	1.27	tuff	canine zone on SW and SE, cup and ring marks
6	1.45	tuff, horizontal layered	bird perch, canine zone on SW side, carved initials
7	0.71	tuff, weathered clasts	bird perch, carved initials
8	0.86	tuff	map lichen follows bedding plane, carved initials
9	1.12	well-rounded tuff	bird perch, canine zone on NE side
10	0.89	tuff, course clasts	pair of diamond motifs on W edge
11	1.32	bedded tuff	canine zone on E side, spiral motif on W side
12	1.22	bedded tuff	pronounced bird perch and canine zone on east side
13	0.99	fine tuff, angular clasts	polished, used as seat, carved initials
14	2.29	tuff and andesite lava fragment	canine zone SW, polished ledges, chipped SE
15	0.74	lava	polished top, chipped edge
16	1.93	andesite lava	map lichen, chipped edge, bird perch, canine zone SW
17	1.73	lava	bird perch (birds face N!), west side polished
18	0.81	tuff, angular clasts	leaning inwards, used as seat, chipped
19	1.32	lava?	bird perch
20	1.47	lava	bird perch, very little canine zone, chipped
21	1.57	andesite lava	bird perch, canine zone on SW side, chipped
22	0.86	lava?	little canine zone
23	1.64	well-rounded tuff	bird perch, pronounced canine zone on SW side
24	0.97	lava	climbed on, lichens much abraded
25	0.42	course tuff, angular clasts	polished, used as seat
26	0.33	tuff	polished, used as seat
27	0.40	tuff	polished, used as seat, diamond motif NE side
28	1.37	lava	bird perch, leaning out, samples chipped off edges
29	1.27	lava	crottle on top
30	0.92	dark lava	samples chipped off
31	0.72	dark lava	samples chipped off
32	0.84	dark lava	crottle in crevices
33	1.14	dark lava	samples chipped off
34	0.45	tuff, matrix wearing proud	polished
35	0.58	tuff	polished
36	1.22	tuff, vertical bedded	little canine zone
37	0.40	tuff?	little canine zone
38	0.07	?	worn smooth, no lichen
39	0.05	?	worn smooth, no lichen
40	0.15	?	worn smooth, no lichen
41	0.71	lava	polished, used as seat
42	0.50	tuff, angular clasts	polished
43	0.69	fine tuff, water lain	polished
44	0.91	tuff, angular clasts	polished, little canine zone
45	0.91	course tuff, large clasts	polished, no canine zone, map lichen prominent
46	0.84	tuff, vertical layered	polished
47	0.38	tuff, fragments proud	totally polished
48	0.91	dark lava	leaning N, good map lichen
49	0.76	dark lava	occasional bird perch, good map lichen
50	0.94	tuff with angular clasts	bird perch, pointed top, canine zone on W side
51	0.91	bedded tuff	map lichen dated 1766, suggestion of spiral motif
hidden outlier	0.70	?	no bird perch, no canine zone (no access for dogs)
2nd outlier	1.00	lava	good lichen cover, pronounced canine zone SE side

Figure 4.2 Summary of the characteristic features recorded for each stone

Acarospora fuscata
Buellia aethalia
Caloplaca holocarpa
Candelariella vitellina (bird perch and canine zone)
Fuscidea cyathoides

Lecanora gangaleoides
L. muralis
L. polytropa
L. solalifera
L. sulphurea
Lecidea fuscoatra
Lecidella scabra
L. stigmatea
Melanelia fuliginosa
Miriquidica leucophaea

Mycoblastus sanguinarius
Ochrolechia androgyna
O. parella
Parmelia omphalodes
Parmelia saxatilis ('crottle')

Pertusaria corallina
P. lactea
P. pseudocorallina
Protoparmelia badia
Ramalina farinacea
Rhizocarpon geographicum (map lichen)

R. reductum
Scoliciosporum chlorococcum
Tephromela atra
T. grumosa
Xanthoparmelia conspersa
Xanthoria candelaria (bird perch)

Figure 4.3 Lichen checklist for Castlerigg Stone Circle (data from the British Lichen Society Summer Workshop 2002)

important to take into account the orientation of the sun and prevailing winds (this is one reason why _Candelariella_ is better developed on the south-facing sides of stones). As a general rule, the distribution of yellow lichen, and in particular, _Candelariella_ species, indicates which stones are favoured by perching birds and visitors' dogs (the yellow band around the base of a stone is the 'canine zone'). It is interesting to speculate on why certain stones are favoured more then others, and why a particular side. A lack of lichen is as important to record as is its presence. Why, for instance, are some stones _less_ attractive to birds and dogs? There is also the human factor – certain stones are given more attention than are others as shown by the degree of polishing, abrasion and soil erosion around their bases. Why does everyone head directly for stones 13 and 14?

The canine zones are more developed on stones in the north-east and south-east quadrants. This would suggest that most visitors start at the 'entrance stones' 1 and 2 and then take a clockwise route around the circle.

Figure 4.2 shows that surfaces that are just short of a metre in height are regularly used as seats whilst those with suitable ledges are frequently climbed on. Certain stones have also attracted the attention of geologists. Many of the stones composed of lava show evidence of being chipped with a hammer.

Since the eighteenth century, the circle has attracted an increasing number of visitors. This has resulted in the removal of many lichens. The outlier by the south-west entrance receives the least attention and its lichen-cover is left reasonably intact. The most recent lichen checklist for Castlerigg has only 32 species (Figure 4.3), almost half that for 'Long Meg and her Daughters' (see Coppins and Gilbert 1987). This may in part be due to differences in geology and rainfall, but it must also reflect the different numbers of tourists visiting the two sites.

Bibliography

Anderson, W.D. (1914) Some recent observations at the Keswick stone circle. *Transactions of the Cumberland and Westmorland Antiquarian and Archaeological Society* **XV** (New Series): 99-112.

Anderson, W.D. (1922) Plough Markings on Stones *Transactions of the Cumberland and Westmorland Antiquarian and Archaeological Society* **XXIII** (New Series): 109.

Beckensall, S. (1997) Initial report following discovery of motifs. Cumbria Records Office, Kendal.

Beckensall, S. (2002) *Prehistoric rock art in Cumbria*. Tempus Publishing. 70-77.

Coppins, B.J. and Gilbert, O.L. (1981) Field meeting near Penrith, Cumbria. *Lichenologist* **13**: 191-199.

British Lichen Society Summer Workshop 2002 – *Cladonia The Lake District (Blencathra) BLS Bulletin* **92**: 42-59.

Dymond. C.W. (1881) A stone circle near Keswick. *Transactions of the Cumberland and Westmorland Antiquarian and Archaeological Society* **V** (Old Series): 40, 50-55.

Fraser, D. *et al.* (1986) Castlerigg Stone Circle documentary and field surveys. Draft Report for English Heritage.

Hutchinson, W. (1794) *The History of the County of Cumberland* **II**: 192. EP Publishing in collaboration with Cumberland County Library (1974 reprint of original published by Jollie, Carlisle (1794-1797).

Lefebure, M. (1970) *Cumberland Heritage*: 133. Victor Gollancz.

Stukeley, W. (1776) *Itinerum Curiosum* **2**: 48.

Warren, A. and Sasitorn, D. (2003) *North-west England from above*. 1, 8. Myriad Books.

Winchester, V. (1988) An assessment of lichenometry as a method for dating recent stone movements in two stone circles in Cumbria and Oxfordshire. *Botanical Journal of the Linnean Society* **96**: 57-68.

5. Walla Crag – the Sign of Eight

Exploring the vegetation and rocks of Keswick's favourite cliff

Checklist:

Distance: 3 miles.

Ascent: 980ft (300m).

Approximate Time: 2.5 to 3 hours.

Maps: 1:25 000 OS Explorer OL4. 1:50 000 OS Landranger 90. 1:50 000 British Geological Survey, England and Wales Sheet 29, Keswick.

Terrain: Steep ascent of Cat Gill. Well-defined paths on rock, grassy ridge and forest track. The narrow path along the cliff edge north of the summit is exposed in places and requires care in strong winds.

Equipment and Books: Hand lens, binoculars, and fungus identification guide.

Footwear: Boots.

Parking: Great Wood car park (NY272214).

Public Transport: Buses from Keswick to Seatoller. Stagecoach Service 77/77A and 79. John Hoban Service 892 (School Bus).

Refreshments: Keswick.

Every time I visit Walla Crag, it always seems to be sunny. So it was, on a brilliant April day, I left the car park in Great Wood and crossed the road to join the shoreline path. I turned left at a group of Scots pine. Their roots had been exposed well above the ground as a result of fluctuations in the lake level and erosion from wave action.

I followed the path across a footbridge. This section is well-known to geologists as a junction between two major rock types (see Shackleton 1966). I walked along the water's edge as far as I could before reaching a slippery grey outcrop shouldering out into the lake. This was the edge of the **Skiddaw Group rock**. At this point I retraced my steps back to make my way up over a rocky path towards the road. The rock was now a distinctly reddish-purple colour. This was the Borrowdale Volcanic Group. It contains haematite, which gives it the blood-red colour (from *haima*: the Greek word for blood). Some sections on the path had angular fragments of grey Skiddaw Group rock enclosed within the volcanic matrix. Geologists have called this '**explosion breccia**' because it was thought to have formed from fragments that were blasted away from the sides of the volcanic vent as the magma broke through the Skiddaw sediments 450 million years ago.

On reaching the road, I crossed at the stile to enter the field opposite.

Picturesque and decaying birches on the ascent of Cat Gill. Falcon Crag can be seen in the background.

A group of large boulders just up from the wall offers shelter in wet weather. I took the path leading left towards Cat Gill. I passed a group of picturesque birch trees to the right of the path. Most were now decaying due to fungal attack. The rotting stems and twigs were covered in thumbnail-sized brackets. Some of these had crennelated, concentric brown bands covered in a thick layer of hairs, giving it the name: *Trametes hirsuta* ('hirsute' being the polite word for 'hairy').

I followed the path as it climbed close to the wall and crossed the narrow footbridge over Cat Gill. From the middle of the bridge I was able to look down on the large oak on the left, growing up from the gill below. Its branches were covered in polypody fern (*Polypodium vulgare*).

I climbed a series of stone steps. This was the start of the new path along the east bank of the gill. There were some fine views across to the right where the steep gill sides were lined with larch, ash, oak and wych elm. Many of these trees had a covering of ivy.

As I approached a gate, I noticed the trunk of an oak to the left of the path. It had **eight parallel grooves** in its bark sloping up the fellside. What could have caused such damage? Once through the gate, I spotted the same effect on four more oaks to the left of the path. The path now

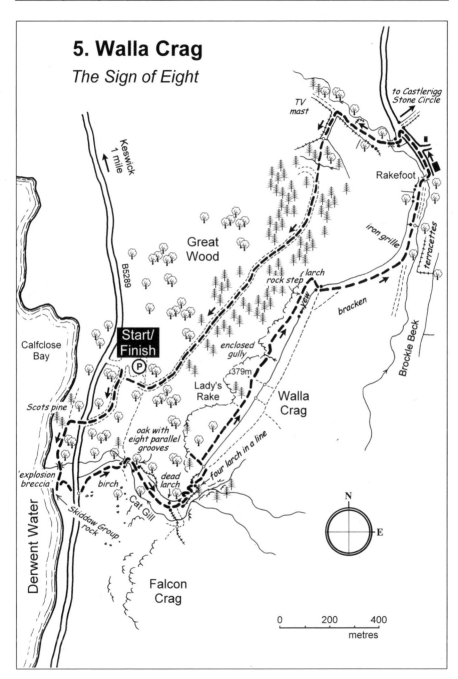

5. Walla Crag
The Sign of Eight

to Castlerigg
Stone Circle

TV
mast

Keswick
1 mile

Rakefoot

iron grille

terracettes

Great
Wood

B5289

larch
rock step

yew

bracken

Brockle Beck

Calfclose
Bay

Start/
Finish
P

enclosed
gully

379m

Lady's
Rake

Walla
Crag

Scots pine

oak with
eight parallel
grooves

four larch in a line

N

E

explosion
breccia

birch

dead
larch

Cat Gill

Skiddaw Group
rock

Derwent Water

Falcon
Crag

0   200   400
metres

followed a wall on the left. On the other side of the wall: another oak and then a birch – both showing the same 'sign of eight'. On passing the next gate, two ash trees were marked the same way. All had the same parallel grooves running uphill.

The path climbed steadily. Ten metres before the next gate, I stopped to look over the wall at a **dead larch**. It was peppered with holes where it had been attacked by bark beetles. All the holes emerged on the south and south-east side where the trunk had been exposed to sunlight.

I couldn't stop puzzling over the eight parallel lines. Several metres past the gate, the wall ended and the path climbed a set of rock steps. I was about to find the answer. Where the path turned right, a young rowan had the same eight grooves – but the evidence of what had caused them was still here

The path made its way through gorse, bell heather and wood sage. **Four larch** had the same marks. They were in a line – and that was the key – all the marked trees were growing *in a line* [see 'Solutions for an explanation].

A gate led out onto open ground with dramatic views across to the waterfalls and larches at the top of the gill. The path climbed a zigzag route alongside a fence and then turned left along a wall to a stile. I crossed the stile and carefully made my way along a short narrow path amongst bilberries and larch towards the cliff edge. This is a favourite viewpoint. To the left I could see Falcon Crag: below me was Derwentwater. The cliff was also a favourite place for the local ravens. On the ground, just back from the edge (above a juniper) I found their pellets.

I retraced my steps away from the edge, but turned left before reaching the stile. A narrow path led through bracken. It descended towards **Lady's Rake**, passing birch and larch growing on the cliff edge. And then a short climb brought me to the summit platform of Walla Crag.. The aerial view over Keswick just had to be photographed. A light breeze made conditions perfect for a group of paragliders who were preparing to leap off the top. I continued following the path along the cliff edge. This was a magnificent section with a feel of real mountaineering. I dropped down to where a stream disappeared over the edge. From a dry wind-swept ridge I had suddenly descended into an **enclosed gully**. The steep sides were lined with greater woodrush (*Luzula sylvatica*). The wet path crossed a step in the rock covered in liverwort

Further along the rocky path, the birch trees gave way to bare rock and then a covering of bell heather (*Erica cinerea*) on the drier slopes. Two ravens flew past in close formation. They were part-folding their wings and performing half-rolls. Never a complete roll, and always to the left!

The view over Keswick from the top of Walla Crag

Are there left-handed and right-handed ravens? Perhaps the direction of the roll relates to wind direction?

The cliff-top path ended at a grove of yews. The path now became indistinct and descended a steep **rock step**, skirting above a group of larch. It then wended its way back to a gate in the summit wall. A broad grassy path led gently down towards Brockle Beck. At this time of evening in April, the sun was catching the grass slope on the far side of the beck. The result was a criss-cross pattern of horizontal shadows. This terraced effect is common on grass slopes that approach a 45 degree angle. The soil becomes unstable and 'creeps' downhill to form horizontal ridges or 'terracettes'. The effect is reinforced by sheep, which follow the same lines.

Where the wall and path turn left to the farm at Rakefoot, the ground becomes deeply rutted. These are grooves left-over from 1944 when the area was used as an Army training ground. A length of **iron grille** that had helped vehicles cross the deep mud can still be found.

I followed the path to the farm, over the bridge and onto the road. Before reaching the signpost and the turn-off to Castlerigg Stone Circle, I took a sharp left turn through a gate (signpost: Public Footpath Keswick Great Wood). The path crossed a footbridge and followed a pleasant riverside path before turning left towards Great Wood. I crossed the stile and after 150 metres joined the forest road that led gently back down to my starting point at the car park.

Taking it Further

For a more detailed account of the geology of the eastern shore of Derwentwater, see Smith 1996.

There is an interesting change of name on modern OS maps. Calfclose Bay would appear to be a typographical error. It was originally named 'Scarfclose Bay' on first and second edition maps. In support of this, there is a rock called 'Scarf Stones' just out from the shore to the west (grid reference: NY263211).

'Scarf' is derived from a vernacular name for a 'Cormorant' – a fish-eating bird that would have been fairly common along this stretch of Derwentwater (see Hutchinson 1794). The same bird is named 'scaw' in Norway, and 'skarfur' in Iceland. There is often confusion between the inland cormorant (*Phalacrocorax carbo*) and the smaller, more oceanic species known as the shag (*P. aristotelis*). This is reflected in the name 'Strandshag Bay' a little further north (grid reference: NY265221).

Bibliography

Hutchinson, W (1794-1797) *The History of the County of Cumberland*, **I**: 455. Jollie, Carlisle. Republished by EP Publishing Ltd. In collaboration with Cumberland County Library (1974).

Shackleton, E.H (1966) *Lakeland Geology*: 26-31. Dalesman Publications.

Smith, A (1996) *The Rocks and Landscape of the Keswick area*. Cumbria RIGS Group.

6. Combe Gill – the Forgotten Valley of Borrowdale

A botanical and geological field trip

Checklist:

Distance: 4 miles.

Ascent: 790ft (240m).

Approximate Time: 4 hours.

Maps: 1:25 000 OS Explorer OL4.
1:50 000 OS Landranger 89 or 90.
1:50 000 British Geological Survey,
England and Wales Sheet 29, Keswick.

Terrain: Easy gradients, apart from the climb up from the packhorse bridge. The approach is mostly over faint grassy paths that become wet and indistinct around the valley head. The return path is well trodden where it joins the path from the Glaramara ridge.

Equipment and Books: Hand lens, compass, moss and lichen identification guides.

Footwear: Boots.

Special Considerations: Please take care not to remove or damage any of the moss or lichen found on the ancient pollards.

Parking: Seatoller National Trust car park (NY245138).

Public Transport: Buses from Keswick to Seatoller. Stagecoach Service 77/77A and 79. John Hoban Service 892 (School Bus).

Refreshments: Yew Tree Tea Room, Seatoller. The Flock Inn and the Scafell Hotel, Rosthwaite.

Here is a valley in Borrowdale where you will hardly meet a soul. You leave the busy road and cross fields and a bridge that are hardly ever crossed. You follow tracks that only sheep have followed and enter a glacial landscape that escapes everyone's camera.

Few venture into The Combe, except for the curious – intent on exploring Dovenest Caves – and *they* run the risk of never coming back! Hill walkers tend to follow the paths onto the summit ridge of Glaramara and stay clear of the valley head.

Here was a place away from the crowds – and the fact that it was labelled on the map as *The* Combe meant that it had to be good.

And so, on a busy September weekend, I set out from Seatoller car park along the footpath that takes you around the back of the Glaramara guest house, across **Folly Bridge** to join the road at Mountain View.

From here I turned left along the road for 200 metres. There was a gate on the right with a **signpost** that simply read 'Public Footpath' pointing the way across a flat field. A path of faintly bruised grass led towards a group of mature oak and alder. It was late summer, and the leaves of the

One of Borrowdale's pollarded ash. The alkaline bark is covered in mosses, liverworts, lichens and ferns.

alder were being eaten by metallic-green leaf beetles. A few metres further and I reached a packhorse bridge covered in maidenhair spleenwort and herb robert. On the up-stream side of the bridge grew a pollarded ash and from that moment I knew the walk was going to be special.

Pollarding is a way of managing trees to produce new branches out of reach of grazing animals. It involves cutting off all the growth every 15 to 20 years at a height of about two metres. The result is a tree that lives twice as long as an uncut 'standard' or 'maiden'. More importantly for the botanist, it provides one of the richest habitats for tree-living ferns, mosses, liverworts and lichens. This 'Cropping Ash', as it is known, is found at its best in upper Borrowdale. It was worth stopping here a while to see what all the fuss was about.

There are three important factors for an epiphyte growing on a tree: rainfall, sunlight and the acidity (or pH) of the bark. Here, in one of the wettest parts of the Lake District, there is over 2400mm of rain per year – perfect for plants such as lichens that have no root system. Pollarding lets the sunlight into the crown and along the trunk – essential for photosynthesis. And delicate surface plants require the bark pH to be within a very specific range. Ash is alkaline compared with oak and this leads to a rich variety of plants colonising its surface.

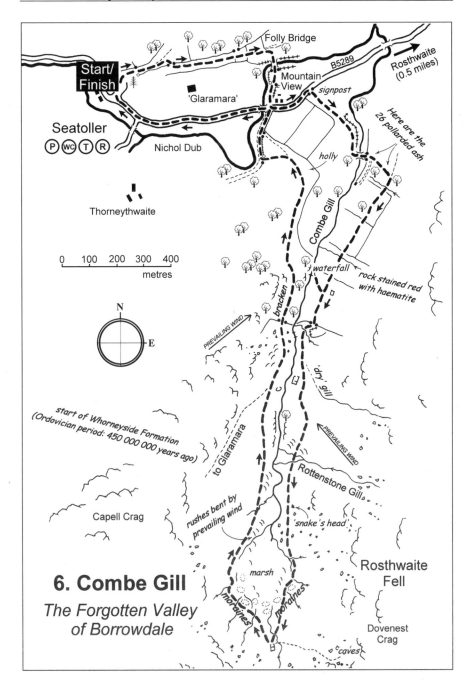

6. Combe Gill

The Forgotten Valley of Borrowdale

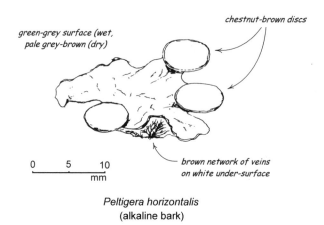

green-grey surface (wet,
pale grey-brown (dry)

chestnut-brown discs

0   5   10
mm

brown network of veins
on white under-surface

Peltigera horizontalis
(alkaline bark)

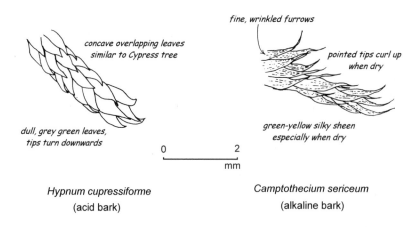

fine, wrinkled furrows

concave overlapping leaves
similar to Cypress tree

pointed tips curl up
when dry

dull, grey green leaves,
tips turn downwards

green-yellow silky sheen
especially when dry

0   2
mm

Hypnum cupressiforme
(acid bark)

Camptothecium sericeum
(alkaline bark)

Figure 6.1 Indicators of acid and alkaline bark

On the pollarded ash next to the bridge grew the moss *Camptothecium sericeum* (see Figure 6.1), a plant characteristic of alkaline bark. It has a golden sheen when dry that resembles embroidered silk. On its surface was the lichen *Peltigera horizontalis* – also an indicator of alkalinity and associated with 'ancient woodlands'. This lichen has a leafy form with chestnut-brown discs along its edge. Its upper surface is grey-brown when dry, becoming greener when wet. Its under-side is white with a brown network of veins.

The route from here had been redirected to climb a steep gravelly slope following a series of yellow waymark arrows. Fifteen metres up this slope from the bridge, I came to a quite different ash with a large swollen boss at its base. This was not pollarded to the same degree as the other and the bark was covered in a dull-white crust of lichen more often seen on oak. The moss, *Hypnum cupressiforme*, was dull green with over-lapping leaves that resembled a 'cupressus'. No yellow silk. No *Peltigera*. This ash was acid!

I continued climbing. In front the ground was divided into three distinct corridors: bracken on the left, a wet flush of loose rocks down the middle, and a strip of grass with ant-hills to the right. The surface stones down the middle were continuously flushed with acid water forming an insect-eating red carpet of sphagnum and sundew.

All around this area were isolated ash: some with alkali and some with acid bark. What was causing the variation? I continued upwards until I reached a signpost where a faint path led off to the right. I passed through a gap in a wall and noticed up ahead a particularly good example just left of the path. This grand old tree was carrying its own ecosystem. In the rotting crown was a polypore fungus together with wood sorrel and dog violets. There was also the silky yellow-green moss covered with *Peltigera*.

On this sloping ground above the packhorse bridge, I counted 26 ash. This was a medieval landscape that had maintained a continuity of tree management. Some of the oldest specimens have been regularly pollarded for over 400 years. [For a more detailed study of this group of trees, see 'Taking it Further'.]

The path now crossed a number of small streams with exposed fragments of volcanic **rock stained red with haematite**, Once through a gap in a second wall I could hear the rush of water in Combe Gill. I had reached the broken walls of an old sheep shelter and at this point was able to make a short detour to the right, down a grassy tongue towards the gill. Here I could look down a slanting gully onto a **waterfall** – an unexpected feature hidden amongst the birch and ash.

I climbed back up the grassy tongue to continue my progress up the valley. The narrow path lead to a well-built wall with a gate. A large boulder to the left of the gate was formed of volcanic ash and debris that had been overwhelmed with water just after it was erupted. The resulting rock is known to geologists as 'lahar' and contains a jumble of fragments or 'clasts' carried along within the flowing mud. Here, the muddy matrix was more resistant to weathering and the clasts could be seen as shallow depressions on the surface.

Once through the gate the atmosphere completely changed. Here the grass was littered with boulders. The path became a sheep track keeping above and parallel with the river, and the river became a series of cascades. The sudden change was due to the exposure of rocks from a more violent period of volcanic activity – the 'Upper Borrowdale Volcanic Series'. Many of the rocks in this area were a pale biscuit-colour and had a glassy texture. This type of rock is known to geologists as 'rhyolite'. It is quite different from the dark course-grained lava found, for example, in the Bowder Stone lower down the valley. Four hundred and fifty million years ago, the lava had become more acid due to an increase in silica. This produced a stickier treacle-like mixture that tended to explode into the air, finally landing downwind as fine ash with angular fragments or bombs. A glance at the geology map showed I had entered the 'Whorneyside Formation' – just glad it was Ordovician, and I was upwind.

I approached a large rectangular **sheepfold** with fine growths of woolly hair moss and cup lichens on the top of its walls. There was no obvious path here. After passing the fold I gained height gradually, climbing away from the river with its tree-lined gully. I aimed for a position where the bracken gave way to grass along a level sheep track. A gentle descent led into Rottenstone Gill, crossing a series of hollows filled with rushes. The stems of this rush, *Juncus effusus*, when exposed to the constant bending forces of the prevailing wind, will set their shape into a curve. The record is kept within last year's dead stems which remain attached. As I looked up the valley, they were all bending towards me from left to right.

The route passed close to the river under a distinct patch of bracken. The going now became easier over undulating grass scattered with boulders. My attention was drawn to a split rock that resembled a **snake's head** with its mouth wide open. There is something exciting about approaching an isolated mountain boulder for the first time – like a detective approaching a crime scene! Here was a fragment of volcanic ash and debris that had once flowed some distance as a wet deposit before solidifying. The section that tapered to form the neck of the snake showed the once-horizontal layers containing a mixture of coarse and fine particles. The remainder of the head and mouth showed less evidence of flow and had a more even mixture of rounded pebbles. From a geological viewpoint, the whole rock could be described as a 'coarse tuff' that has been sorted according to particle size. But these volcanic particles also varied according to chemistry. The clues were there in the lichen. The distinct bands at the back of the snake's head were covered in rusty brown colonies with darker spots (*Lecidea* species), whilst the remainder of the head had a pale green map lichen with black spots (*Rhizocarpon* species). The lichen indicated iron in the neck and silica in the head. Some snake! The top of the head was covered in yellow *Candelariella* – showing it to be a favourite perching site for the local birdlife.

I continued over the grassy slopes weaving my way between yet more boulders. And then, over the next grassy rise, the scene changed dramatically. There was the illusion of an enclosed stretch of water with pale basin-shaped hills emerging through its surface and around its shoreline. Between 11 000 and 10 000 years ago, this valley head was covered in a layer of stationary ice. One theory suggests that material from the surrounding cliff edges broke away and fell onto its surface. On melting, the debris was dumped to form this hummocky moraine. In support of this view, it is interesting to note that there are no hummocks in the centre, only around the edges – which is where the material would have fallen. Whatever the theory, the results are spectacular – a 'lake' of rushes with its shoreline of rounded hills – held in a jagged amphitheatre of rock slabs.

The ground was very wet and care was needed to skirt the rush flats and negotiate the hide-and-seek **moraines** before reaching another rectangular sheepfold. Readers of Wainwright will recognise this as the staging-post *en route* to Dovenest Caves (Wainwright 1960). I decided to stop at the sheepfold and have lunch. This was certainly a forgotten valley. I hadn't met a soul since leaving the main Borrowdale road. The only object moving was a wren that had taken up residence in the nearby stone walls. I sat perfectly still and could hear it calling and flitting in and out of the gaps. Wainwright describes Dovenest Crag as a 'a stiff climb of ten minutes' from this fold (see Wainwright 1960). He also describes the **caves** as being a good diversion for a wet day. Looking up towards them, I could see the route up the red scree that extends down from the steep grassy slope. There were some interesting slabs of rock with glistening white facets where sheets of quartz had become exposed. The fertile soil nearby had patches of Alpine lady's mantle.

 The route back presented some interesting ecological puzzles. As I left the fold and approached the first moraine, I crossed an area of wet grass that had strange rings of tall grass, from ten to twenty centimetres in diameter. In the centre of each ring was a dead stem from which the tall grass radiated outwards. If I had been here in spring or early summer, the puzzle would have been solved straight away! But In late summer, the evidence was not so clear.

The way back around the rush flats on the west side of the valley needed care. By following the edge of the rushes I was able to join a narrow sheep track. I was keeping an eye on the rushes. They all recorded the same wind direction – that is, they all faced north-west. What was unexpected was a prevailing wind that did not blow straight down the valley but veered up the slope to my left. Then a surprise. As I approached the main fell wall, the rushes switched direction and faced north-east! At this particular spot, the prevailing wind turns ninety degrees and is deflected off the valley side like a billiard ball from a cushion.

Why are there rings of tall grass left in an area grazed by sheep? Top photograph taken late summer, lower photograph taken early spring. [See 'Solutions' for an explanation.]

Once through the gate in the wall, I entered waist-high **bracken**. The wind had been almost eliminated from this section. I followed the sheltered path through an area of birch and hazel, eventually joining a wall on the right with the occasional **holly**. One of these female trees was covered in berries. The leaves at the base of the canopy had plenty of spikes whilst those higher up were smooth. This distinction is frequently seen in holly. It is thought to 'respond' to grazing animals by producing more protective spikes – but only in those leaves where they are needed.

I continued following the wall until I reached a stile. This lead onto the farm road that took me back to Mountain View. The quickest route back to Seatoller was the footpath alongside the main road.

Taking it Further

The locality of the 26 ancient ash seen on this walk is shown in Figure 6.2. The survey details are given in Figure 6.3.

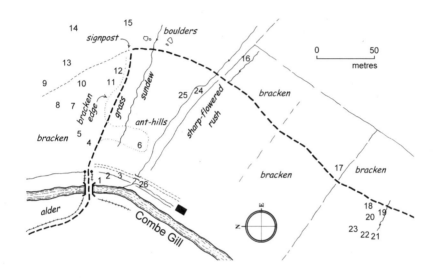

Figure 6.2 The localities of the 26 pollarded ash

There are many questions that remain unanswered. To what extent is genetics responsible for bark pH? What is the contribution of environmental factors such as soil chemistry and moisture, degree of pollarding, levels of sunlight, pollution etc? Do trees maintain the same acidity or does this change over time? Does acidity correlate with the timing of spring growth? (On this latter point, it is noticeable when visiting the site in early April that some of these ash develop their leaves much earlier than others.)

The main indicator of acid bark is the dull grey-green moss *Hypnum cupressiforme* which supports the lichens *Cladonia corniocrae* and *Parmelia saxatilis*. Dull-white crusts of *Pertusaria* lichen are often found growing directly on the bark.

Tree No.	Plant species growing on base of trunk	Properties
1	*C. sericeum, P. horizontalis*	alkali
2	*H. cupressiforme, P. saxatilis*	acid
3	*C. sericeum, P. horizontalis*	alkali
4	*Pertusaria* sp.	acid
5	*H. cupressiforme, C. sericeum*	acid/alkali?
6	*H. cupressiforme, Pertusaria* sp.	acid
7	*H. cupressiforme, Pertusaria* sp.	acid
8	*H. cupressiforme, Pertusaria* sp.	acid
9	*H. cupressiforme, C. sericeum*	acid/alkali?
10	*H. cupressiforme, Pertusaria* sp.	acid
11	*H. cupressiforme, Pertusaria* sp.	acid
12	*H. cupressiforme, Pertusaria* sp.	acid
13	*H. cupressiforme, Pertusaria* sp., *C. sericeum, P. horizontalis*	acid/alkali
14	*H. cupressiforme, Pertusaria* sp., *C. sericeum, P. horizontalis*	acid/alkali
15	*H. cupressiforme, Pertusaria* sp., *P. saxatilis*	acid
16	*H. cupressiforme, Pertusaria* sp., *C. sericeum, P. horizontalis*	acid/alkali
17	*H. cupressiforme, Pertusaria* sp., *C. sericeum, P. horizontalis*	acid/alkali
18	*H. cupressiforme, P. saxatilis*	acid
19	*H. cupressiforme, C. sericeum, P. horizontalis*	alkali
20	*H. cupressiforme, P. saxatilis*	acid
21	*H. cupressiforme, Metzgaria furcata*	acid
22	*H. cupressiforme, P. saxatilis*	acid
23	*H. cupressiforme, P. saxatilis*	acid
24	*H. cupressiforme, Pertusaria* sp., *P. rufescens*	acid
25	*H. cupressiforme, Pertusaria* sp.	acid

Figure 6.3 Field observations on the 26 pollarded ash

Alkaline bark is characterised by the silky yellow-green moss *Camptothecium sericeum* which supports extensive patches of *Peltigera*, most notably, *P. horizontalis* (see Gilbert 2000).

The survey in April 2003 recorded a ratio of approximately three acid to every one alkaline tree (only trees with *P. horizontalis* were recorded as alkaline – see Figure 6.3.). This ratio has been found in other parts of Borrowdale (Day 1989). It would be interesting to know if this is a fixed ratio that applies to the whole of western Britain, and if the ratio is changing.

Bibliography

Day, I.P. (1989) *Seatoller Woodlands, Seathwaite, Borrowdale, Cumbria. Lichenolgical survey of pollards and other ancient trees.* Report to the National Trust, Keswick.

Gilbert, O.L. (2000) *Lichens.* HarperCollins, London.

Wainwright, A.W. (1960) *A Pictorial Guide to the Lakeland Fells: Book Four, The Southern Fells*, Rosthwaite Fell; 3. Westmorland Gazette, Kendal.

7. Eskdale – a Problem at Doctor Bridge

A riverside walk and an architectural puzzle

Checklist:

Distance: 3 miles.

Ascent: Negligible.

Approximate Time: 2 hours.

Maps: 1:25 000 OS Explorer OL6.

Terrain: Level footpaths apart from a section after Girder Bridge which involves a short, steep climb away from the river to reach the upper path.

Equipment: On a warm day, swimwear and towel.

Footwear: Boots.

Special Considerations: The mine workings are flooded and dangerous and exploration is not recommended.

Parking: Car parks at Dalegarth Station (NY174007) and Trough House Bridge (NY172003).

Public Transport: Ravenglass and Eskdale Railway (Telephone enquiries: 01229 717171).

Refreshments: The Woolpack Inn (for that after-swim brandy!)

It was some years since I had lived and worked in Eskdale and my return visits are always nostalgic. I had decided to look over some of my favourite haunts along the River Esk. Trough House Bridge, Girder Bridge and Doctor Bridge, held many memories. I thought I knew the area fairly well but it was only recently, whilst researching the County Records, that I found out how Doctor Bridge got its name.

And so on a hot summer's day, I set off to investigate. I started from the little-used car park at Trough House Bridge. Before crossing, there was the evidence of past valley floods carved on the right-hand sandstone pillar. On the 10th of August 1962, the level reached the top of the parapet!

One hundred and fifty metres past the bridge, I turned off down the lane following the signpost to St Catherine's Church. After a gate, the path wended its way between mossy walls lined with coppiced hazel and the occasional sycamore, and after 500 metres I turned right to join the narrow road that led past the church.

The River Esk was directly ahead and I turned left along a stony path to follow its northern bank. Over the wall on the left grew a number of mature birch. Some were infected with the white razor strop fungus. The next gate led to an interesting junction for this is where the **old railway** line came to take iron ore from a number of levels on the south bank of the river. The track had gone but the route it once took could still be seen. The parallel stone walls on the left lead all the way back to the Ravenglass and Eskdale Railway terminus at Dalegarth. Interestingly, this section leading to the river was built without Parliamentary permission (see Adams 1995). The path now followed the **old track bed** along a delightful section of river with clear, deep pools and fast flowing rapids.

"Jump in here!"

I can still here the words of Jeff Lee, the former warden of Eskdale Youth Hostel, teaching his assistant warden to swim. After all, he was over six-foot and don't argue. And he was standing with his feet on the bottom, head above the surface – there would be no

St Catherine's Church

This restored 14th-century church still has its original east window. The churchyard has 103 different species of lichen – the fourth-highest number recorded for a Cumbrian church.

problem. The problem was, I was five foot nine and had negative buoyancy. At least we could laugh about it afterwards over a resuscitating brandy!

The Girder Bridge, as I remember it in the 80s, was just two iron girders that had once supported the railway track. Now it had a planked surface with handrails and gates at each end. I wanted to see if there were still signs of a river crossing used by the Outward Bound School a few metres upstream from here. To the left of the bridge was a group of mature trees including **three larch**. I examined the one growing about 15metres back from the edge. It had a prominent side-branch facing the river. Around its trunk at a height of one metre and half a metre from the ground I found the evidence: four horizontal bruise marks left on the

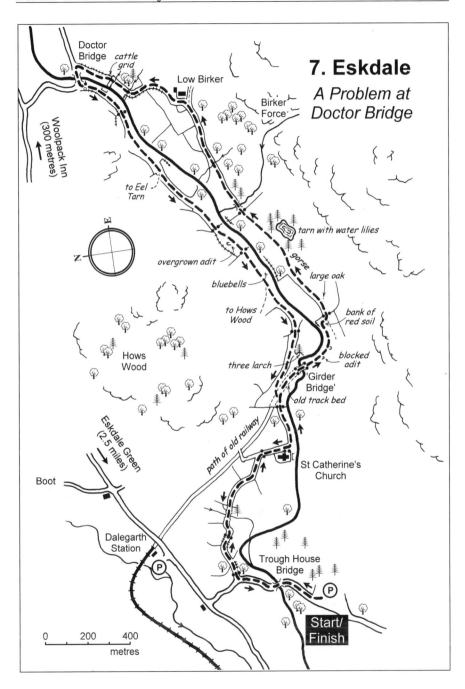

7. Eskdale
A Problem at Doctor Bridge

bark by climbing ropes. Excellent! I rushed across the bridge to check the other side. An old oak with two trunks joined at its base was growing on the edge of the riverbank. The right-hand trunk had a rope groove just above the base. And that was it; just as I remembered, as no doubt did the eight Outward Bound students that I was assisting back in July 1986. The task was to get all eight team members safely across the river: a sort of low-level 'Tyrolean Traverse' (The high-level Traverse was above Stanley Ghyll.). The ropes were secured between the two trees and a sliding transporter system made of rope was used to pull each team member across in turn. The secret was to attach the rope high enough up the trunk of the larch to allow for the sagging in the rope.

I continued along the path above the south bank of the river. For 70 metres I followed the railway bed. There were patches of bright red soil from the haematite that was mined here. The railway line led into a **blocked adit** on the right. A stream was issuing below a crescent-shaped opening and an oak was growing alongside with its roots being undermined. I continued another 70 metres to a where a second stream crossed the path. This was issuing from a deep drainage channel that led to two flooded adits. Ten metres further I reached a bank of red soil and climbed a narrow path away from the river, following the wall on my left. I joined the higher path, which took me left through a gate in the wall. In front was a **large oak** surrounded by ant-hills. I continued on past gorse, past a spruce plantation hiding a secluded tarn with water lilies, a gate in a wall and then over a narrow footbridge. Great views across to the north; another stream crossed, and then the left fork in the path as I dropped down to Low Birker. On the outside of the garden wall, alongside the garden gate, was a 'pot crane': an iron bar that was once swung across an open fire to suspend pots for cooking. A farm road with an open field on the right – another gate – a plantation of birch, larch and oak – **cattle grid** – getting nearer the river again – a line of ash, birch and sycamore and finally … Doctor Bridge.

 Sherlock Holmes would have enjoyed this:

"Well, Watson, what do you make of it?"

"A good, solid bridge with a single arch …"

"And the name – what of the name, 'Doctor' Bridge? Why not Farmer Bridge or Nurse Bridge for that matter?"

"You have the better of me there, I'm afraid."

"Look closely at the structure underneath the arch. Do you see it?"

"What am I looking for, Holmes?"

"Do you notice anything odd about the stonework?"

"Only that it's been well maintained."

"Maintained and much more besides!"

"You lose me, Holmes."

"Well, consider the name 'Doctor'. What two things has a country doctor got in the 18th century that a nurse hasn't got?"

"A black bag ... a stethoscope ... a top hat?"

"He may indeed have all these; but with regard to this bridge, the first thing he has is *authority*, Watson! And secondly, and just as important, he owns a ..."

[The 'Solutions' section reveals the answer to this puzzle. But examine the photograph carefully before turning to the back of the book – the clue is there, underneath the arch.]

There was, however, one more puzzle that Holmes hadn't mentioned. As I approached the middle of the bridge, I noticed something on the right-hand parapet. In neatly incised letters facing me, it read: 'DO NOT DAMAGE THE BRIDGE'. Now why should anyone build a plaque into the bridge with all the expense of employing a stonemason to chisel in such a message? Wasn't this a place as far away as you could imagine from 18th-century vandalism? Was there some ill feeling surrounding this bridge that would warrant the building-in of such a message? I left the bridge excited at solving one puzzle but perplexed at finding another.

Doctor Bridge on the River Esk. But how did it get its name?

The return journey along the north side of the river was just as delightful as the approach. Two hundred metres after leaving the bridge, the path goes through a gate. On the right, a side path leads off to Eel Tarn but I kept straight ahead on a level section bordered with gorse. Looking south across the river I had magnificent views of Birker Force over the trees. The level, grassy path continued with a wall on my right and open fields down to my left. After a second gate, the wall was replaced by a wire fence. Ahead of me was a third gate and 50 metres before reaching it I noticed a large ant-hill surrounded by foxgloves just to the right of the path. On closer inspection, I found a faint track lined with broom leading into an **overgrown adit**. One of these adits is reputed to pass under the river, but I wasn't going down there to find out.

I continued on, through the gate into a more open area. Two hundred metres past the gate I could see a dark green patch of vegetation down the slope to my left. With the binoculars, I could make it out to be an isolated circle of **bluebells** growing below a willow. The rest of the sloping ground was full of bracken. What had caused this I wondered? – trampling by animals sheltering under the tree and so keeping the bracken away? Or was it the shade from the tree, or simply a patch of wet ground?

A path branched off to the right to Hows Wood, but I kept straight ahead to eventually join-up with the abandoned railway above Girder Bridge. Just time for a swim for old times' sake before retracing my route back to the car.

Taking it Further

St Catherine's Church is well worth a visit. It has an interesting font with an octagonal bowl that is thought to be fourteenth century. One hundred and three different species of lichen have been recorded from the graveyard: one of the highest numbers recorded for a Lakeland church (see Figure 7.1). The reason for such a high count is unclear. The rainfall is not unusually high: Borrowdale's is higher. It is situated away from the road and so is not subjected to high levels of pollution from car exhausts – but so is Martindale Old Church which has recorded the lowest number for the County. The headstones are mostly local granite – an acidic rock not noted for supporting such an exceptional variety of epiphytes. That leaves two factors that would appear to be paramount – the age of the graveyard and the way it has been managed. In this old churchyard, the surfaces of gravestones have been left undisturbed. In so many other churchyards, the lichens have been simply 'cleaned' away.

Information on lichens in churchyards can be found in the British

Church	grid reference	survey year	number of species
Barton - St Michael	487264	1994	58
Bassenthwaite - St Bega	226287	1992/4	43
Bassenthwaite - St John	229316	1994	42
Brathey - Holy Trinity	362032	1997	55
Brigham - St Bridget	86309	1996/7	142
Broughton-in-Furness - St Mary Mag.	209873	1994/9	106
Buttermere - St James	176170	1995/7	64
Caldbeck - St Mungo	326399	1994	29
Coniston - St Andrew	302976	1995	35
Crosthwaite - St Mary	445912	1994	28
Embleton - St Cuthbert	163294	1991/6	71
Eskdale - St Catherine	176004	196/7	103
Far Sawrey - St Peter	378952	1995	31
Finsthwaite - St Peter	369878	1995	31
Glenridding Methodist	387173	1996	62
Gosforth - St Mary	72036	1996	90
Grange-in-Borrowdale - Holy Trinity	253175	1997	51
Ireby Old Church/Chancel	224394	1993/4	75
Keswick - St John's in the Vale	306225	1995	62
Lorton - St Cuthbert	155259	1995	49
Loweswater - St Bartholemew	142209	1995	71
Martindale - St Peter	435192	1994	22
Martindale Old Church/St Martin	434184	1994	11
Muncaster - St Michael	104965	1997	99
Mungrisedale - St Kentigern	364305	1995/7	86
Patterdale - St Patrick	394162	1996	84
Shap - St Michael	564154	1993/4	56
Threlkeld - St Mary	323254	1994	109
Torver - St Luke	285943	1996	55
Tottlebank Baptist	314845	1997	76
Wasdale Head - St Olaf	188087	1993	37
Windermere - St Mary	409987	1997	63
Wythburn Parish Church	324136	1993/6	89
Wythop - St Margaret	190301	1994	53

Figure 7.1 Number of lichen species recorded in Lakeland churchyards (data supplied by Don Smith, British Lichen Society)

Lichen Society leaflet: *Churchyard Lichens* available on the Society's web site (http://www.theBLS.org.uk).

Bibliography

Adams, J. (1995) *Mines of the Lake District Fells*: 124. Dalesman Publications.

8. Devoke Water – a Bronze Age Secret

Using surface vegetation to interpret the hidden landscape

Checklist:

Distance: 4 miles.

Ascent: 725ft (220m).

Approximate Time: 3 to 4 hours.

Maps: 1:25 000 OS Explorer OL6. 1:50 000 OS Landranger 89 and 96. 1:50 000 BGS. England and Wales Sheet 38, Ambleside. 1:25 000 BGS Sheet SD19, Devoke Water and Ulpha.

Terrain: Level easy-to-follow track to and along south shore of Devoke Water. The remainder of the route is ill-defined over grassy slopes and requires careful map reading.

Equipment and Books: Compass, hand lens, binoculars. *Lakeland Rocks and Landscape: a Field Guide* edited by Mervyn Dodd is particularly recommended for exploring the geology.

Footwear: Boots.

Special Considerations: If you wish to examine the Bronze Age sites in Brantrake Moss, the walk is best undertaken in early spring before the bracken covers the surface. The archaeological features described are Scheduled Ancient Monuments. It is an offence to disturb or deface them or to use a metal detector within two metres of their boundaries.

Parking: Roadside parking for up to 10 cars at junction of Devoke Water track and the Eskdale Green/Ulpha road (SD171977).

Public Transport: None.

Refreshments: Newfield Inn, Seathwaite (Duddon). King George IV Inn, Eskdale Green.

On some walks in Eskdale, the geology and archaeology are unmistakable. Climb north from Boot, for example, and you can hardly avoid the haematite. And the paths south of Burnmoor will lead you to the many stone circles and ancient cairns. Devoke Water provides a different challenge. The evidence is hidden away and the satisfaction comes from finding the clues.

Before setting out, I had studied the geology maps. I had seen the archaeological reports and the aerial photographs of the area. But when I came to interpreting the actual landscape, I could have been on the surface of the moon!

I left the car on the Ulpha to Eskdale Green road at the crossroads where the track leads to Devoke Water. The signpost pointed the way. The geology map showed that I was walking the boundary between Eskdale Granite to the north and the Borrowdale Volcanic Series to the south. The Cumbria Sites and Monuments Record described a

Bronze Age **cairnfield** to the right of the path that contained at least 160 circular and oval 'clearance cairns'.

I decided on a short detour to seek them out. Twenty-four metres past the gate, a faint path led away from the stony track through the grass to my right. Sixty metres along this path, I should have been in the centre of the cairnfield. There were no obvious piles of stones not until, that is, I stopped looking for stones and started looking at the surface vegetation. The wet ground was covered in the fine spikes of 'deer grass' (*Trichophorum cespitosum*), a sedge that is typical of peat moorland. But amongst this uniform landscape were discreet patches of pale-yellow matt-grass, *Nardus stricta* (see Figure 8.1). I was standing in a sea of

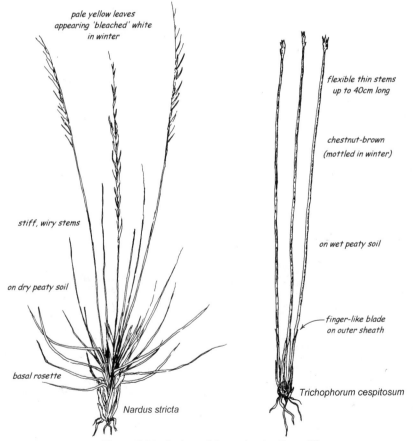

Figure 8.1 Indicators of dry and wet soil conditions

dark-brown sedge surrounded by islands of pale grass, each about two metres in diameter. Amongst the grass, the ancient piles of stones could just be seen breaking through the surface. The hidden cairns were changing the drainage and mineral content of the soil, and the evidence was in the pattern of vegetation.

I retraced my steps back to the Devoke Water track. The wet ground over to the left was covered almost entirely by 'deer grass', indicating an extensive area of peat bog. Within this area were a number of sunken rectangles where peat had been removed. The regular cutting of peat had continued in Eskdale up until the 1920s (Denyer 1991). When opening a peat bog for the first time, the top ten centimetres of turf were removed. It was considered 'good neighbourly' to replace this turf afterwards to avoid leaving a water-filled hollow that would endanger livestock (Winchester 2000). For the same reason, the line of the cut was always up the slope, and a drainage ditch left at the bottom. A cut measuring 20 metres by 10 metres dug to one spade's depth would have produced 10 000 'peats'. In the Outer Isles of Scotland, where peat is still being used, this would keep one fire burning through the year. The volume that needs to be cut is larger than expected. Peat can lose half its volume in

A Bronze Age cairnfield above the Devoke Water track. The cairns can be found underneath the pale circles of matt-grass.

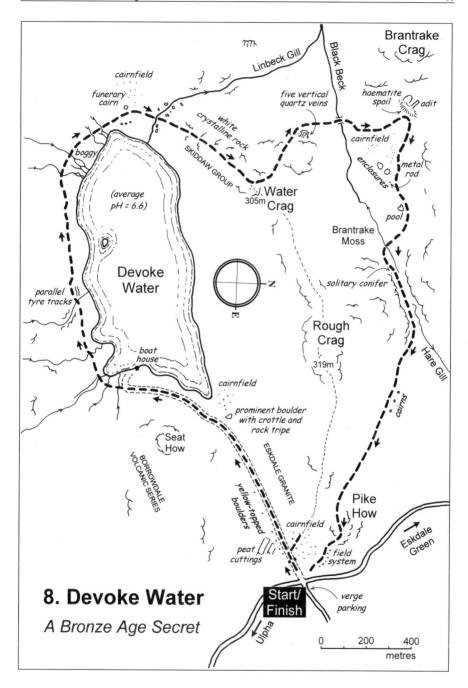

Brantrake Crag

Linbeck Gill

Black Beck

cairnfield

funerary cairn

five vertical quartz veins

haematite spoil   adit

white crystalline rock

SKIDDAW GROUP

cairnfield

enclosures

metal rod

boggy

(average pH = 6.6)

305m Water Crag

pool

Brantrake Moss

Devoke Water

N

solitary conifer

parallel tyre tracks

E

Rough Crag

Hare Gill

boat house

319m

cairns

cairnfield

prominent boulder with crottle and rock tripe

Seat How

BORROWDALE VOLCANIC SERIES

yellow-topped boulders

ESKDALE GRANITE

Pike How

cairnfield

Eskdale Green

peat cuttings

field system

8. Devoke Water

A Bronze Age Secret

Start/ Finish

verge parking

Ulpha

0   200   400
metres

drying – and then the final product produces only two thirds as much heat as coal.

Peat cutting in the Lake District can be traced back to the 16th century, by which time much of the higher ground had been denuded of trees. Pollen analysis from Devoke Water (Pennington 1964) has shown that this upland area was extensively wooded up until the middle Bronze Age. Trees were cleared and stones were piled up in cairns to clear fields for growing crops. In some cases, the stones were thrown up against the sides of trees and when the tree decayed, the cairn was left with a hollow centre. Lines of such cairns have been described as 'fossilising a line of vanished trees' (Clare 1988).

I continued along the straight track. Just off to the left, I kept passing individual boulders about half a metre in height, each with a yellow top. When examined with a x10 hand lens, the yellow was composed of tiny coral-like lumps – a characteristic of the lichen *Candelariella coralliza*. To the right of the track there was a **prominent boulder** approximately three metres long and two metres high. Here was the same yellow top. Below this was a leafy lichen that had white, raised veins on its surface. This was 'crottle' (*Parmelia saxatilis*), once used in Harris Tweed to dye the wool a golden brown. Further down the boulder there were three-inch-wide channels of 'rock tripe' (*Lasallia pustulata*) extending down to ground level (Figure 8.2). This lichen was also used to dye wool, producing delicate shades of pink and mauve. All three lichens grow where there are high levels of nitrogen. Find the lichen and you find where the birds have perched. What is interesting is why they favour some boulders and not others.

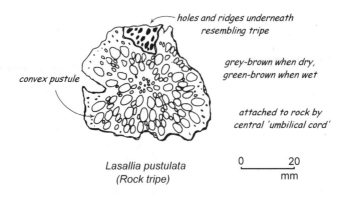

Figure 8.2 Rock tripe – often found in rain channels, on an isolated boulder used as a bird-perch. In the past, this lichen that was used for dying wool, producing delicate shades of pink.

I could now see the **boat-house** up ahead. To the right of the path were more patches of grass amongst the bracken, indicating yet another cairnfield. The track ended at the boat house. From now on the path became boggy and indistinct in places. After crossing several streams, I reached a point half-way along Devoke Water. The shrub-covered island was now about 100 metres away. A stream emerged from a slanting gully on my left and cut across the path. For ten metres this path became a quagmire, before a dry grassy section that continued level with the island. But my attention was on the 'quagmire'! It had two **parallel tyre tracks** that were 1.25 metres apart. I had seen some wartime film footage showing American Willis Jeeps being brought over Walna Scar to Seathwaite, and then being driven along the south side of Devoke Water. They had become bogged-down up to their axles along this section of path. That was back in 1944. For a moment, my imagination got the better of me – could these really be the 'trace fossils' of a 1944 Willis Jeep preserved in the mud? The two mountain bikes on the skyline soon corrected my train of thought!

I continued along the south side of the shoreline to reach the end of the lake. Fifty metres back from the shore on the drier slope were yet more ancient cairns including a large **funerary cairn** occupying the highest ground. Its centre had been made into a modern shelter but its spreading base was reasonably intact. My route now took me north as I dropped down to cross Linbeck Gill and then the climb up the rough slope of Water Crag. Here was a geological oddity. Along this ridge, all the major Lakeland rock types come together at the surface (see Young 1992). Veins of quartz indicate faults that once contained high-temperature liquid rock. This changed the chemistry of the surrounding rocks leaving a mixture of crystalline minerals including topaz. On the climb to the top of Water Crag I expected to find Borrowdale Volcanic rock. It was a complete surprise to find there were

American Willis Jeeps setting off from the Newfield 'Hotel' on a training exercise around Devoke Water in 1944

also outcrops from the Skiddaw Group with their distinct cleavage planes. These rocks showed signs of being baked hard and brittle. The source of this intense heat was the Eskdale Granite, which had left a landscape dotted with **white crystalline rock** faces.

From the summit of Water Crag I looked north across to Brantrake Moss. This is a wilderness that is now hardly trodden but it was once the site of a successful Bronze Age community and a Romano-British farmstead. I knew from the Cumbria Sites and Monuments Record that there was a haematite mine, a cairnfield with associated plough marks, two funerary cairns, two hut circles and two walled enclosures. The two walled enclosures were clear but where were the rest?

There was a large patch of grass amongst the bracken to the east of Brantrake Crag. I decided to aim for that. But first I needed to wend my way down the granite outcrops on the north slope of Water Crag. Three hundred metres after leaving the summit I passed a prominent outcrop that contained **five vertical quartz veins**. From here I made my way down to Black Beck which I crossed at a small plank-bridge. I climbed north through bog myrtle and crossed a swath of grass where I could see evidence of the cairnfield. Then it was more bracken before I reached the prominent grassy area that I had suspected would lead to the mine. At the top of the grassy clearing, I found a ridge of **haematite** spoil and above it a deep trench cut back into the hillside. The entrance was blocked and overgrown. The geology map showed that I was standing on a vein of iron extending northwards from here. About ten metres further west was an intrusion of crumbling rock that had been quarried (marked as iron-rich lamprophyre on the geological map). Could the run-off from this exposed area of mine-spoil, have stopped the bracken and allowed the grass to develop immediately below? Brantrake Moss mine-workings are not well-known outside archaeological circles. Their age is uncertain but they are thought to be late-medieval.

I now made my way to the two most-prominent features on this gently-sloping hill side: the two walled **enclosures** thought to be part of a Romano-British farmstead but now used as a sheep shelter. From here, I walked 50 metres east to find a pale patch of grass, in the centre of which was a **metal rod** projecting through a square of plywood. What purpose could this possibly serve?

The metal rod sunk into the ground at Brantrake Moss

The metal rod had been put here by the local farmer for a specific function and its effect on the surrounding vegetation could clearly be seen [see 'Solutions'].

From here I continued east, skirting around a boggy area with drainage channels and a surface pool of water. This was a remote setting: a shallow valley running up to a valley head that cut through a rock channel connecting Black Beck with Hare Gill. There were no obvious paths except those made by sheep. I made my way up the right-hand side of the channel, passing a prominent, **solitary conifer**. It had been a dry spell and I was able to drop down to follow the lowest part of the channel to its watershed – a raised cushion of sphagnum and rushes. After wet weather, this section could be negotiated by following the higher ground on the right.

Once through the rock channel, I contoured south-east across the moor to the summit of Pike How; its ice-smoothed rocks a favourite haunt of ravens. I looked down at the characteristic rivulets of lichen – with the ravens flying overhead, and thought to myself: "The rock tripe never lies!"

Now I could see my starting point on the road. In front was a Bronze Age **field system**. I followed its western boundary along a wandering line of clearance cairns, and finally dropped down to the crossroads where I had parked the car.

Taking it Further

Sherlock Holmes could provide a psychological profile of a suspect by an examination of discarded tobacco ash. On this walk, the nature detective will be rewarded by the even-more-esoteric study of lichens growing on left-over bird lime! The information could be of use when locating favourite roosting and feeding ledges as well as nest sites. For the botanist, this becomes an exercise in 'phytosociology': the grouping together of plants into communities that are associated with a specific niche. The lichens on bird-perching sites are classified as belonging to the 'Nutrient-Enriched' community of which there are two alliances:

❖ The first is found on silica-rich rocks exposed to sunlight with slight to moderate nutrient enrichment.

❖ The second is found on both siliceous and calcareous rock with high levels of nutrient enrichment – often by the sea coast.

The rocks encountered on this walk belong to the first of these alliances which can be further subdivided depending on the mix of rock tripe, crottle and the yellow *Candelariella* lichens (see James, Hawksworth and Rose 1977).

The tarns of the Lake District have been classified as either permanently acid (pH 4.2 to 5.3) or softwater (pH 5.4 to 7.0). Devoke Water has recorded an average pH of 6.6 which is considerably less acid than would be expected from a rock basin situated on Eskdale Granite. This would suggest that the unusual geology of this region is contributing to its alkalinity, possibly in the form of carbonate or bicarbonate ions (see Sutcliffe and Carrick 1988). The higher the pH generally means the more productive the water, which is shown by a greater number of invertebrates and a more-varied lichen flora around the shoreline (Gilbert 2000).

Bibliography

Clare, T. (1988) In *The Lake District: Landscape Heritage* (Rollinson, W., ed.) David and Charles.

Cumbria Sites and Monuments Record: *SMR Numbers: 9460, 9462, 9463, 1425, 1430.* County Offices, Kendal.

Denyer, S. (1991) *Traditional Buildings and Life in the Lake District.* Victor Gollanz in association with the National Trust.

Gilbert, O.L. (2000) *Lichens*: 224-226. HarperCollins.

James, P. W., Hawksworth, D. L. and Rose, F. (1977) Lichen communities in the British Isles: a preliminary conspectus. In *Lichen Ecology* (Seaward, M. R. D., ed.) 295-413. Academic Press, London.

Pennington, W. (1964) Pollen Analysis from six upland tarns in the Lake District. *Philosophical Transactions of the Royal Society, B* **248**: 204-244.

Sutcliffe, D. W. and Carrick, T. R. (1988) Alkalinity and pH of tarns and streams in the English Lake District (Cumbria). *Freshwater Biology* **19**: 179-189.

Winchester, A.J.L. (2000) *The Harvest of the Hills*: 45-46. Edinburgh University Press.

Young, B. (1992) The Eskdale Granite. In *Lakeland Rocks and Landscape: A Field Guide.* (Dodd, M., ed.): 46-53. Ellenbank Press.

9. Duddon Valley – the Message in the Slate

Exploring the quarry roads of Caw

Checklist:

Distance: 5.4 miles.

Ascent: 1500ft (450m).

Approximate Time: 3 to 4 hours.

Maps: 1:2500 OS Explorer OL6. 1:50 000 British Geological Survey, England and Wales Sheet 38, Ambleside.

Terrain: The quarry roads follow easy gradients over surfaces of loose stone, The ascent of Caw is a steady climb on steep grass with no definite path. The path across the summit ridge is intermittent over grassy slopes with some rocky sections.

Equipment: Camera.

Footwear: Boots.

Special Considerations: Unless you are experienced and fully equipped for underground exploration, entry into the Caw quarry adit is not recommended.

Parking: Please note that parking outside the Newfield Inn is for patrons only. There is space for a limited number of cars in roadside parking places to the north of Seathwaite Church (SD229962).

Public Transport: The Royal Mail Postbus arrives in Seathwaite at 10.15, 1200 and 1715hrs on weekdays (except Thursday and Sunday, and excluding 1715 on Saturday).

Refreshments: Newfield Inn, Seathwaite.

The quarry roads around Caw provide an easy way onto the high ground above the Duddon Valley. The plan was to follow the Park Head Road and the Caw Quarry Road on our way onto the summit ridge, returning via Walna Scar. In April we had to abandon the walk due to strong winds and rain. Now it was mid-October and the weather was perfect.

We arrived in Seathwaite early morning and parked the car just off the road north of the church. Our route began at the bend in the road 150 metres south of the church. There are three sets of farm gates and then a delightful track follows a stone wall as it climbs gently across the west flank of Caw. The path was bordered by a mixture of trees – mostly oak, birch and hazel, with groups of mature sycamore in the fields to our left. Significantly, there were both sheep and cattle grazing in the fields.

The initial period of volcanic activity in the Lake District was characterised by high temperature molten lava – typically producing dark flows of 'andesite'. There was also the occasional violent interlude when fine ash and debris were spewed into the air to settle and consolidate as

The start of the walk – a bright October morning in Seathwaite

'tuffs'. This produced rocks of the Lower Borrowdale Volcanic Series. In the Duddon Valley, however, we would be walking through the Upper Borrowdale Volcanic Series – rock that was formed later, when the volcanoes had cooled down. The silica content had increased leaving a magma that had become more sticky. Now the eruptions were suddenly violent, throwing out successive clouds of ash and debris in huge quantities; falling in layer upon layer, some in dry conditions where the heat welded it back together, some on wet surfaces where it flowed down slopes, and some being reworked and jumbled together form-ing layers of tuffs, sandstones and breccias. The weight of all this mate-rial compressed and folded the underlying rock and realigned its crystal structure to follow the line of pressure. This produced a line along which the rock would split, known as the cleavage plane. This is why the rock was quarried – for the slate.

For the moment, however, at the start of our journey, we were cross-ing fertile **glacial 'drift'**. The deep well-drained soil had extensive patches of bracken and lush grass. This was a favourite place for the yellow meadow ant, *Lasius flavus* – a species responsible for the large domed ant-hills so often seen on dry grassland. As we gained height, the drift became punctuated by rock outcrops that had been smoothed by ice. But where were the meadow ants? Some were amongst the bracken,

Ant-hill at the side of Park Head Road. Why do these meadow ants build their nests on the edges of rock outcrops?

but some of the larger and therefore older colonies had been built on the **bare outcrops of rock**. Some, in fact, were on the very edges of the rock. These weren't 'meadow' ants. These were 'rock ants'! Could this be another example of ants escaping mechanical disturbance? (see Walk 2, Buttermere and references to wood ants at Coldwell Parrock). Could they have colonised the edges of rock outcrops to avoid being trampled by cattle?

When we were here in April, a vertical rock face on the left of the path had split and fallen down. A **holly** that had been growing in the cracked surface had toppled over. Now it was six months later and the tree was still alive, but its leaves were different. The wild holly, *Ilex aquifolium*, has an efficient strategy for producing spikes. Those leaves at the top of the tree have less spikes than those lower down because they cannot be reached by grazing animals and therefore do not need protection. The rock fall had provided a natural experiment and the results confirmed this adaptive process. After the tree had fallen, some of the smooth leaves in the canopy could be reached by sheep and were now being heavily grazed. The holly had responded by replacing the grazed leaves with new growth covered in spikes!

(Thirty metres past the holly, a small stream crosses the path and

flows under a short section of plank fence. If you reach this without
seeing the holly – you have gone too far.)

The path continued close to the wall, making only a short detour
around a rocky bluff. Two hundred metres further we passed an interesting gap stile that had been built into the wall top. The rocks here were
showing more signs of cleavage and the change was visible in the rocks
used in the wall. We continued through a gate and then past a sheepfold
with nettles outside the entrance. It's strange how nettles always find soil
with high levels of nitrogen.

The trees had dwindled to just the occasional isolated juniper and
holly. The turn-off to Caw quarry was now only 50 metres away and the
colour of the path suddenly changed. We were crossing a seam of **red
microgranite** (the same seam, or 'dyke', that shows up in the path outside
High Wallowbarrow on the opposite side of the valley). After a slight
climb, we reached the junction leading to the quarry and turned left.
This was a well-engineered section that had been terraced to make it as
level as possible for quarry ponies. We passed an impressive needle of
rock about three metres high that had split away from the rock wall on
the right: another reminder of the distinct cleavage plane running
through these rocks.

The quarry road led to a massive pile of slate spoil. A grassed-over
track climbed off to the right and then left to reach a group of quarry huts.
To the south of these we found the quarry **adit** – a horizontal tunnel tall
enough to stand up in. From the entrance we shone a torch inside. The
beam of light hit the back wall about 15 metres away. At that distance
there appeared to be a T-junction with galleries opening up to the left and
right. Judging by the amount of spoil from this one entrance, these galleries must have been quite extensive.

At this point on our previous visit, bad weather had forced us to abandon the walk. Now, on this bright, clear Autumn day, we headed up the
grass to the right of the adit, keeping left of the small stream. The path
was indistinct but the route was without problems, winding between
rocky outcrops to reach the Ordnance Survey column on the summit.

Caw is not at the top of the fellwalker's list. It was a surprise, therefore,
to find that the summit rocks had been carved with so many dates and
initials. The earliest date that could be made out was 1870. And yet this
was not part of the Victorian 'grand tour'. Perhaps the summit once held
a special significance for the local population? The view was certainly
special: all the favourite fells around the head of Eskdale from Crinkle
Crags to Scafell; a peep into Devoke Water and the gash of Wallowbarrow

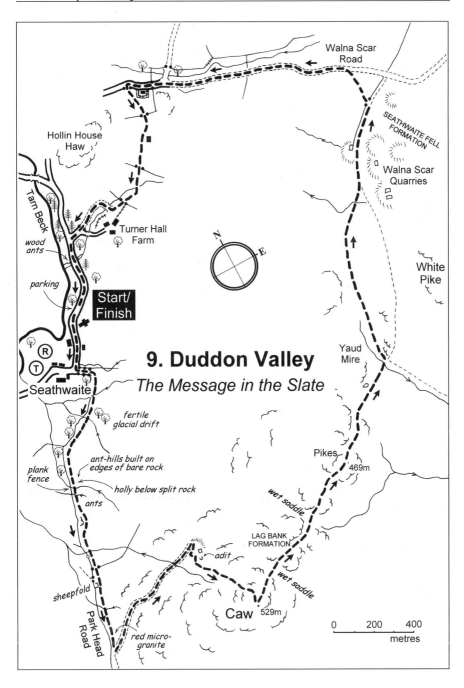

Walna Scar
Road

SEATHWAITE FELL
FORMATION

Hollin House
Haw

Walna Scar
Quarries

Tarn Beck

wood
ants

Turner Hall
Farm

White
Pike

parking

N

E

**Start/
Finish**

R

T

Yaud
Mire

Seathwaite

9. Duddon Valley
The Message in the Slate

fertile
glacial drift

Pikes
469m

ant-hills built on
edges of bare rock

plank
fence

wet saddle

holly below split rock

ants

LAG BANK
FORMATION

adit

wet saddle

sheepfold

Caw 529m

0   200   400

metres

Park Head
Road

red micro-
granite

From the top of Caw looking south-west across the Duddon Estuary

Gorge. But the view that really held the eye was to the south – across the Duddon Estuary and down to Morecambe Bay. The sun was glinting off the sea, and the slight haze added a horizontal wash of pink that merged into bands of blue and grey.

Our next summit was Pikes. A faint path led away from Caw in the direction of Walna Scar. We dropped down to a wet saddle before climbing past a small pool. Two hundred metres further and the volcanic rocks had changed, with thimble-sized lumps weathering out from their surfaces. The geology map indicated that we had crossed into the **'Lag Bank Formation'** formed of fine ash containing small rock fragments known as 'lapilli'. We dropped down to cross another wet saddle, aiming slightly right over sphagnum and rushes to follow a narrow, level path. The next set of rocky knolls brought us to the well-named summit of Pikes.

The intermittent path now led across the wet depression known as Yaud Mire. We crossed a stream to join the rutted path leading north below White Pike. This led to the massive spoil heaps of Walna Scar Quarry – a major source of building slate for this area. The quarried slabs came from rock known as the **'Seathwaite Fell Formation'**. The volcanic ash of 450 million years ago settled in water and the subsequent movements and currents produced a series of fluid features more often associated with sedimentary rock. Different coloured layers of fine ash were

laid down in horizontal beds. Some of these were later folded: some were disrupted by faults. The result was a highly decorative surface that reveals itself along the cleavage plane. The best examples were used in the floors of many of the local houses. The characteristic parallel banding can still be seen in pieces of discarded spoil.

We followed the quarry track alongside the wall and then turned left through a gate. A faint track cut the corner across tussocky grass to join the main Walna Scar Road. After threequarters of a mile we reached the metalled road. Two hundred metres further, we turned left through a gate in the roadside wall. The route back took us

Walna Scar Slate on the porch floor of the Newfield Inn. These slates were formed from fine volcanic ash laid down 450 million years ago. The parallel beds of dark and light-coloured ash contain excellent examples of geological folds and faults.

across level fields to Turner Hall Farm to join the valley road. Before reaching the car, the road crossed a stream, and just before crossing the stream on the right there was a pile of pine needles spilling out onto the road edge. This was another ant nest, only these ants were much bigger than those seen on the outward journey. This was a **colony of northern wood ants,** *Formica lugubris,* thought to have been introduced in Victorian times to provide food for pheasants. The ants escaped and colonised the woods around Seathwaite.

10. Coniston – the Stone of Malachi

The environmental effect of 'heavy metals'

Checklist:

Distance: 5 miles

Ascent: 2130ft (650m).

Approximate Time: 5 hours

Maps: 1:2500 OS Explorer OL6. 1:50 000 British Geological Survey, England and Wales Sheet 38, Ambleside.

Terrain: A gentle approach on quarry roads changes to a steep rough ascent over loose spoil and rock steps to reach Levers Water. The approach to the Black Scar Workings has no definite path.

Equipment: Hand lens and pH paper.

Footwear: Boots.

Special Considerations: Please do not remove any large samples of malachite from the spoil heaps but leave them for others to enjoy. To avoid walking in shadow, this walk is best done early morning.

Parking: Public car parks in Coniston. Space may be available on roadside on approach to Dixon Ground (SD300975).

Public Transport: Buses from Kendal (through Windermere and Ambleside) to Coniston. Stagecoach Service 505, 'The Coniston Rambler'.

Refreshments: The Wilson Arms in Torver provides some of the best bar meals in the district.

There are many hundreds of adits, quarries and vertical shafts in the Coniston hills but one in particular caught my eye. The Black Scar Workings below Little How Crags was different. It was one of the region's earliest workings, and more significantly – it was a source of malachite.

It was early morning, April and clear as a bell. I had studied the map and decided on a route. I started outside the Sun Hotel and followed the lane (signpost: Levers Water), passing the house with the name Dixon Ground. The lintel over the doorway was a slate slab that looked like a guitar case with two holes. It had been a gate post. The two holes had once received the hinges and the wide end had been set in the ground.

On the other side of the road, I passed through a gate into a grass field. A track led to a bridge made of a single piece of slate bordered by railway sleepers. Amongst the trees to the left I could see another bridge that once carried the railway. A quick glance at the map showed that this was the terminus of the former branch line.

The stony track passed through a delightful wooded section with the deep gorge of Church Beck down to the right. After a gate, the track

Coppermines Valley. The Youth Hostel is centre-left. Simon's Nick is on the far-left skyline.

became a narrow stony path that led to Miners Bridge. I crossed over and continued on the unsurfaced 'road', following the east side of the beck. In front of me was an industrial landscape of spoil heaps, quarry roads and mine workings. On the skyline to the left of the Youth Hostel was the distinctive gash of Simon's Nick, marking one of the most productive veins of copper found in the valley.

Four hundred metres after crossing the bridge, and just off to the left of the 'road', I reached an area of spoil alongside a ruined mine building. I was standing next to what looked like giant Christmas puddings, each 0.6metres in diameter, each left as if it had just been tipped out from a basin. Their surfaces were black and red and slightly polished.

These were **abandoned 'casts'** of the smelted copper and iron ore. Assuming each cast to be a hemisphere with a specific gravity midway between iron and copper (see Taking it Further), each cast weighed 480 kilograms or nearly half a ton – some pudding!

The road led to the Youth Hostel where I joined a quarry track following the north-east bank of Church Beck. After approximately 400 metres, a junction led off to the left. I ignored this and continued following the track as it climbed gently to the right for a further 200 metres to a wooden footbridge. I crossed the bridge and then turned right to follow the narrow path up the west side of the beck. The next section was a steep climb across the base of the spoil-heap below Simon's Nick. It led to a grassy, level section at the edge of Levers Waterfall. This was a good place to get a breather and check out the local lichens.

One of the first things I had read about lichens was their sensitivity to metals. Copper and iron would generally be regarded as toxic. It doesn't take much iron to stop plants from growing. That is why, on a wire fence, you don't see lichens covering the rusty wire, or even the wood in contact with the wire. Well, that was what I thought. But now I was to find that things were not that simple.

With my back to the waterfall, I approached the base of the spoil heap. Some of the larger pieces of spoil, about the size of a bucket, had black lustrous patches. This was rock that contained sulphides of both copper and iron. Geologists recognise these in the form of chalcopyrite and **goethite** (the latter named after the German poet who was a keen mineralogist). This kind of rock is extremely acidic due to the local production of sulphuric acid. Surely nothing could grow on this?

I looked closely at the bucket-sized rocks. They were covered in bright orange and dull browny-red patches of what appeared to be rust. But on looking again with a hand lens, the rust turned out to be lichen! This was no ordinary lichen. It belongs to a group called the

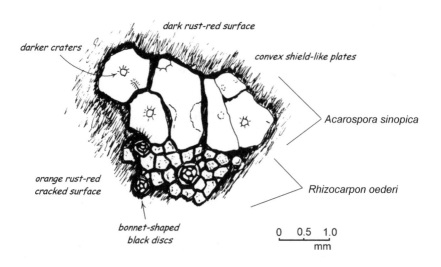

Figure 10.1 The *Acarosporion sinopicae*. These lichens specialise in colonising iron-rich rock.

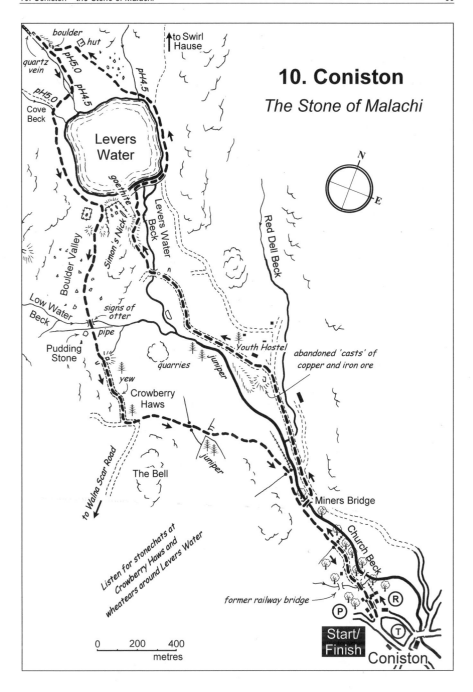

boulder
hut
to Swirl
Hause

quartz
vein
pH5.0
pH4.5
pH5.0
pH4.5
pH4.5
Cove
Beck

10. Coniston
The Stone of Malachi

Levers
Water

N

E

goethite
Levers Water Beck
Simon's Nick
Levers Water Beck
Boulder Valley
Red Dell Beck

Low Water Beck
signs of otter
pipe

Pudding
Stone
quarries
juniper
Youth Hostel
abandoned 'casts' of
copper and iron ore

yew
Crowberry
Haws

to Walna Scar Road
juniper
The Bell

Miners Bridge

Church Beck

Listen for stonechats at
Crowberry Haws and
wheatears around Levers Water

former railway bridge

P

R

Start/
Finish

T

Coniston

0   200   400
metres

Acarosporion sinopicae that specialises in colonising iron-rich rock in well-lit conditions (see Figure 10.1). If there is life on Mars – this surely has to be it!

The path continued over a steep rocky section before levelling-out into a grassy area with scattered boulders. In front of me was Levers Water. I followed the path around the edge of the dam and continued along the north-east shoreline. Across the other side of the water on the opposite skyline I could see the rocky slopes of Little How Crags. One third down from the ridge I could just make out a vein of white quartz that indicated a major fault-line that ran underneath Levers Water. This was the 'Paddy End Vein' and it ended on Little How Crags at an old mine called the 'Black Scar Workings' (see Holland 1982). It is here that the copper appears as malachite a form of the metal composed of copper carbonate. More interestingly, the copper ore is alkaline.

I had brought some pH paper that was accurate to 0.1. Levers Water gave a reading of 4.5. I was hoping that the readings would rise dramatically as I approached the source of the malachite.

I crossed the stream coming down from Swirl Hause – pH 4.5. There was no clear path along this next section as I began to climb away from the shore over an undulating grassy slope dotted with large boulders. I looked across to Little How Crags and could clearly see the dark entrance to the malachite mine– a vertical shadow to the right of the quartz vein. I avoided a direct line and aimed off to the right towards a ruined building. This was a miners' hut, its slate roof long gone, but with walls still intact. It had two rooms. The south-facing side of the partition wall was encrusted in silvery-grey 'eruptions' of a lichen often found on metal-rich rock. Its name is *Stereocaulon* – from the Greek word 'stereos' for solid or stiff, which describes how the plant holds its stalks stiffly away from the rock surface. This is significant when the rock contains high concentrations of metals. It is as though the plant is holding itself away from the toxic surface to reduce its contact to a minimum.

Now I made my way across to the foot of the mine. I had travelled approximately 100 metres from the ruin when I reached a small stream barely a metre wide. I was directly in line with the ridge of spoil coming from the mine entrance. The pH read 5.0. This was it! The increase in alkalinity meant I was getting closer to the malachite. I reached a boulder about the size of a garden shed. It was at the foot of the line of spoil, which was piling up against its upper side. Looking up the ribbon of spoil from here, it was bordered on the left by a stream, and on the right by a ridge of grass. The area had been well picked-over by geologists and at first there were no obvious signs of any tell-tale green patches – only chunks of broken quartz. But as so often with something new, it was just a matter of 'getting my eye in'. I concentrated on a small area by my feet and carefully turned over each piece of rock that had a fragment of quartz. And there it was – green malachite – some small shiny patches and the occasional velvety texture with ripple marks where the mineral had evaporated leaving a characteristic series of concentric bands.

The mine entrance was 150 metres above me. I tested the stream to my left: still pH 5.0. The entrance was a narrow vertical gash to the right of the **quartz vein**. There was no sign of copper ore inside on the surface rocks. The pH of the dripping water was a disappointing 4.5. But the conditions on the right of the opening were perfect for bilberries – and unlike most areas of Lakeland fell, this patch could not be reached by sheep and was completely ungrazed.

I made my way back down the spoil to the large boulder. I followed the stream over rough grass and scattered boulders. The pH of the stream dropped to 4.5. The rocks had a covering of *Stereocaulon* and rusty *Lecidea* species, indicating high levels of metals. Approximately 100 metres from the Levers Water shore, I crossed Cove Beck. Significantly, this had a pH of 5.0! Was this evidence of a hidden source of malachite in the stream above?

I had now joined the narrow path above the south-west shore of Levers Water. The boulders were covered in the familiar crottle, growing with a slightly unfamiliar hue. The 'leaves' of this lichen are usually a pale turquoise occasionally tinged dusky red where birds have perched. But on this shaded side of the valley, they appeared to have a deeper blue tinge. Could this be the reduced amount of sunlight? I had a fanciful thought that it might be the copper. That would have been convenient – using the lichen instead of pH paper!

The path brought me back to the southern end of the water. This was an area with many vertical shafts that had been recently fenced-off. I made my way between the two fenced enclosures. The path then passed between two small spoil heaps with goethite-stained rocks covered in the same *Acarosporion* alliance I had seen below Simon's Nick. A glance at the OS map showed I was about to enter 'Boulder Valley'. The geology map indicated that I was crossing a layer of Borrowdale Volcanic rock called the 'Paddy End Member' – rock that was formed from ash that had welded together in a sticky treacle-like mass. The large boulders at the side of the path had rippled surfaces: an indication that this 'treacle' must have flowed some distance before setting.

The path led to a wooden footbridge across Low Water Beck. The rocks lining this water channel were a stark, uniform grey. The dry surfaces projecting above the water looked as though they had been bleached – no lichen, just the colour of the rock. And the rock here was 'slate'.

By habit, I looked under the bridge to check for **signs of otter**, and to my surprise, one of the rocks had a cap of dark-green algae. There were no spraints, but this rock showed all the signs of being regularly dosed with nitrates and phosphates!

Once over the bridge, I passed the Pudding Stone – the largest named-boulder in the Lake District after the Bowder Stone. The rough, stony path then climbed for 50 metres before descending a flight of stone 'steps': a series of flat rocks that had been skilfully jammed into a steep cleft. The path led to a platform of slate spoil, which marked the start of the quarry road over Crowberry Haws. This was a wonderful section – a gently descending terrace bordered by juniper. On this April morning, I could hear stonechats calling close by. Where the quarry road bends slightly to the right, there was a **yew** overgrowing the road side. A narrow band, extending one and a half metres above the ground had been grazed by sheep, and in response, the foliage had grown tightly-packed like a hedge.

At a junction with another quarry road, I turned left. After only 15 metres, I joined a faint path leading away to the left (take care here – if you find yourself following the right-hand bend in the quarry road, you have gone too far). I followed the narrow path, dropping gently towards Church Beck. On reaching Miners Bridge, I retraced my route back to the starting point at the Sun Hotel.

Taking it Further

The pH readings were taken in April. The values will be lower than the yearly average following the high rainfall and effects of snowmelt over the winter months. An increase in water-flow results in a dilution of the mineral content. The pH of Lakeland tarns and upland streams tends to increase throughout the summer as the mineral content increases (see Sutcliffe and Carrick 1988).

The range of pH measured in the streams above Levers Water may not appear to be very large. A difference of 0.5 does not seem much. But unlike the linear scales that we use in day-to-day life, the pH scale is logarithmic (pH = negative logarithm of the hydrogen ion concentration which causes acidity). This means that an increase in pH from 4.5 to 5.0

is a *3.2 fold* decrease in acidity (4.0 to 5.0 is a *ten fold* decrease, whilst 4.0 to 6.0 is a *one-hundred fold* decrease).

The weight of the metal 'casts' found on the road side before reaching the Youth Hostel was calculated as follows:

Assuming a density of 8.5g/cm^3 for a mixture of copper and iron (9.0 for copper and 7.9 for iron), and assuming the volume of each 'cast' to be an approximate hemisphere with a 30cm radius.

Volume of hemisphere = 1/2(4/3 πr^3)
                     = 1/2(4/3 π30^3)
                     = 56548.67cm^3

Mass = Volume x Density
     = 56548.67cm^3 x 8.5g/cm^3
     = 480.66kg

When discussing their toxic effects on the environment, copper and iron are often referred to as 'heavy metals'. The term is used regularly in popular language when discussing environmental issues. It also persists in the scientific literature despite there being no scientific basis for linking 'heaviness' with 'toxicity' (see Duffus 2002). Lead, copper and mercury are undeniably 'heavy' in terms of their density. But where do we place aluminium and beryllium which can also be toxic in certain forms? Both are among the 'lightest' metals known! The matter is further confused when we equate the biological effects of the pure element with its compounds. Pure metal is rarely a danger to a living organism. Tin only becomes a serious threat to marine life in the form of 'tributyltin oxide'. Chromium causes little harm in stainless steel but is toxic as a 'chromate'.

The environmental effects of iron and copper depend upon their chemical form. Compare the conditions produced by the oxides and sulphides at Simon's Nick with those produced by the hydrated carbonates at the Black Scar Workings. The lichen distribution provides an interesting insight into these differences. A distinctive group of lichens, the *Acarosporion sinopicae* alliance, has been found where the metals are present as sulphides, in extremely acidic conditions (see Gilbert 2000). But where copper occurs as carbonate, in alkaline conditions, there is a completely different group of lichens that forms the *Lecideion inopis* alliance (Purvis and James 1985).

The growth of such specialised plantlife on mineral-rich rock makes a challenging study. Do these 'metallophytes' grow here because they can *tolerate* the toxic effect of metal compounds, or are they actually *dependent* upon them for their growth?

Bibliography

Duffus, J.H. (2002) "Heavy Metals" – a meaningless term? (IUAPC Technical Report), *Pure and Applied Chemistry* **74**, (5): 793-807.

Gilbert, O.L. (2000) *Lichens*: 179-180. The New Naturalist Library, HarperCollins.

Holland, E.G (1982) *Coniston Copper Mines. A Field Guide.* Cicerone Press.

Purvis, O.W, and James, P.W. (1985) Lichens of the Coniston Copper Mines. *Lichenologist* **17**(3): 221-237.

Sutcliffe, D.W. and Carrick, T.R. (1988) Alkalinity and pH of tarns and streams in the English Lake District (Cumbria). *Freshwater Biology* **19**: 179-189.

11. Whitbarrow – a Lesson on Limestone

A walk along Lakeland's fossil coastline

Checklist:

Distance: 5 miles.

Ascent: 560ft (170m).

Approximate Time: 3 to 3½ hours.

Maps: 1:25 000 OS Explorer OL7.

Terrain: Ascent involves steep woodland paths on limestone rock (slippery when wet). Whitbarrow top is a dry, level promenade.

Equipment and Books: Hand lens, wildflower guide, Cumbria RIGS booklet: Whitbarrow.

Footwear: Boots.

Special Considerations: This is a quiet rural area. Please keep dogs on leads, particularly near farm buildings.

Parking: Car park at end of lane (SD437859).

Public Transport: Buses from Kendal to Barrow, Stagecoach Service X35 pass by Witherslack. Kendal to Cartmel, Service 530 goes to Witherslack road end.

Refreshments: Derby Arms Hotel.

We had planned a walk on Whitbarrow with our friends, Mike and Cath. It was another fine September afternoon and the wind was getting up from the south. Perfect walking weather: 12 degrees, no midges. We parked the car in the lane outside Witherslack Hall grounds, and crossed the cattle-grazed pasture in the direction of the football pitch. The path led behind the **goalposts** and climbed diagonally up through the woods. The climb began gently enough over exposed tree roots, and then became steeper as we picked our way over the steps of Dalton Limestone that make up the west face of Whitbarrow Scar.

As we gained height, the view over the woods opened out, with the towers of Witherslack Hall prominent below. There were a few occasions when the view disappeared completely, as we became enclosed by yew trees. This was hardly the yew forest of old – but these remnants were some of the best-preserved examples of yew woodland in the Lake District. It had an eerie atmosphere: sinuous trunks emerging from a seemingly dead forest floor.

The path led to a stile in a wall. An information board indicated that we were about to enter the Hervey Nature Reserve (Canon Hervey was the founder of the Cumbria Wildlife Trust). Here was a landscape of

Wind-blown yew on Whitbarrow Scar

limestone scree with scattered silver birch and juniper. The wall on our left marked the edge of the cliff with magnificent examples of **wind-blown yew**. Does any other tree develop such a dramatic shape in response to the wind? The prevailing wind along this coastline is south-west, and Whitbarrow is the first cliff to intercept it. Yew is one of only three 'conifers' native to Britain (the others being Scots pine and juniper). It develops an unusual cross-section, showing a distinct change from the dark-brown heartwood to an almost white sapwood. The heartwood resists compression and the sapwood resists tension. It is this special property that makes it an ideal wood for the longbow.

We dropped down gently from the path to examine the wall. The exposed surfaces of each piece of limestone were completely covered in lichen. A hand lens revealed a living mosaic of grey, black, white, yellow and even pink! Some of these lichens had eaten into the rock to form tiny pits. Crossing this miniature landscape was the snail *Punctum pygmaeum*, only 0.2 mm long with a tongue small enough to reach down into the pits and crevices.

We continued along the path. Scattered amongst the loose pieces of limestone we found harebells with a particularly deep-blue flower. The ant-hills were covered with eyebright, wild thyme, spring sandwort and fairy flax: classic limestone flora, but all this was about to change.

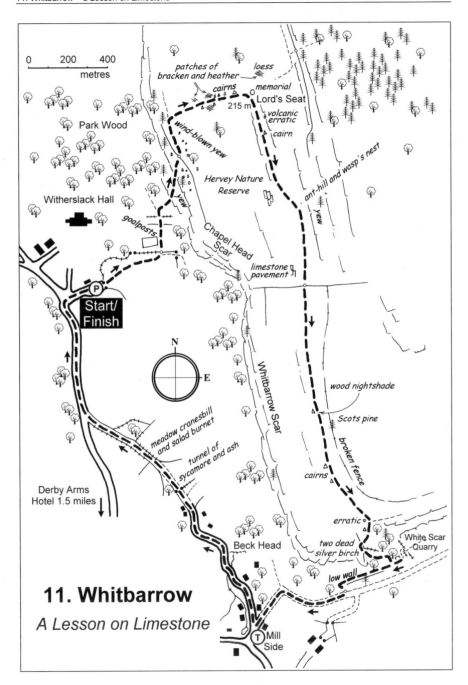

0   200   400
metres

patches of
bracken and heather
cairns
loess
memorial
Lord's Seat
215 m
volcanic
erratic
cairn

Park Wood

wind-blown yew

ant-hill and wasp's nest

Witherslack Hall

Hervey Nature
Reserve

yew

goalposts

Chapel Head
Scar

limestone
pavement

P

Start/
Finish

N

E

Whitbarrow Scar

wood nightshade

Scots pine

meadow cranesbill
and salad burnet

tunnel of
sycamore and ash

broken fence

cairns

Derby Arms
Hotel 1.5 miles

erratic

White Scar
Quarry

Beck Head

two dead
silver birch

low wall

11. Whitbarrow

A Lesson on Limestone

T Mill
Side

Photomacrograph of *Punctum pygmaeum* found on Whitbarrow's limestone wall. (The size is indicated by the pin head in the bottom-left corner.)

The path branched off to the right, following a series of cairns. Along this section there were isolated **patches of bracken and heather** with the yellow flowers of St John's wort. We were walking on solid limestone with a pH of more than 8 and yet here were islands of soil with a pH of less than 6. On closer inspection, the soil turned out to be sand – blown in from Morecambe Bay! After the last glaciers had retreated from the Cumbrian coast, the fine silts and sands were exposed in estuaries that extended right up to the foot of Whitbarrow. The prevailing winds of 10 000 years ago were from exactly the same direction as those experienced today. The result was blown sand – what geologists call 'loess', which drifted over the limestone surface and settled in the shallow depressions.

The path led us to the summit and the Canon Hershey memorial cairn. Close by, near a low wall, grew a struggling elder bush covered in the lichen, *Xanthoria polytropa*, ('xanthos' in Greek means yellow). It was bright yellow today, but in wet weather it turns a distinct shade of green.

From the memorial we followed the broad path heading south along the ridge. Just before reaching a prominent cairn, we noticed an isolated boulder across to the left of the path, It was approximately one-metre long and a darker colour than the surrounding limestone. This was a volcanic erratic that had been transported here by ice from the central

Lake District. It was covered in colonies of map lichen. One part of its surface in particular caught my eye. An oval area about the size of a saucer had colonies that were about 30mm in diameter – much smaller than colonies found elsewhere on the surface.

"Someone thirty years ago thought this an interesting rock for study." [See 'Solutions']

The path now dropped gently towards the two-metre-high scarp edge. This was one of the distinct bands of Urswick Limestone that crosses the summit of Whitbarrow. Each band had taken up to half a million years to form from the shells of creatures living in the sea 350 million years ago. Just before reaching the scarp edge there was an ant-hill to the left of the path. A woodpecker had been at work and had uncovered a wasp's nest within the ant-hill. The fragments of the nest resembled crumpled tissue scattered amongst the hollowed-out mound.

Sixty metres further, we passed a line of yews growing along the scarp edge. They were bent horizontal by the prevailing south-westerlies. The path veered over to the right towards an area of **limestone pavement**. The top surface of the limestone had been dissolved by acid water leaving raised blocks or 'clints' and deep grooves known as 'grykes'. Where the surface was tilted, there were meandering grooves or 'runnels' where the water drained away. You can tell the direction of flow when you see a runnel shaped like a 'Y' or a 'V': flowing water tends to coalesce into a single channel. At the bottom of the grykes we found hart's tongue fern – the only fern that has a continuous, unbranched leaf.

We crossed the wall at the gap stile. The north-facing side was coloured black and the south-facing side dove-grey. (Every rock surface in the Lake District seems to be covered in lichen, and limestone is no exception.). The path followed the line of an old wire fence over to our left. The yellow flower in the path was rock rose. The tomato-like flower at the next cairn was wood nightshade. This plant belongs to the same family as deadly nightshade. In autumn, it forms poisonous red berries. No one seems to have told the crows – their pellets were full of them! After passing an isolated Scots pine we reached another cairn. Alongside were the silver-haired fruit of 'old man's beard', *Clematis vitalba*. Another cairn: a burdock growing through the gaps in the stones. But now it was the view over the Kent Estuary that caught the eye.

The next landmark was just off to the right of the path – another volcanic **erratic**. Our path now took a turn to the right, descending through patches of birch and bracken (waymark arrows point the way here for

The giant brackets of *Ganoderma applanatum* on birch (© C. Mortimer 2002)

those climbing Whitbarrow from this side). After passing through a gap in a wall (more way-mark arrows), the path cut back through a second gap and continued on the east side of the wall. Where the path veered away from the wall, I noticed two dead **silver birch**, fifteen metres off to the right. Cause of death? – *Ganoderma applanatum*, normally found causing 'white rot' in beech. Here it had attacked birch. The brackets were huge (please do not remove if they are still attached) – like dinner plates sticking out from the trunk; creamy-white underneath, a fine white rim and a rough brown-grey upper surface. Underneath were the spores, like a fine dusting of cocoa powder.

After passing another way-mark arrow, the narrow path descended through woodland until it emerged at a clearing by a seat. Once again there were magnificent views across the Kent estuary. A wide path led across left to the disused **White Scar Quarry**, which could be reached through a gap in a fence. It had the atmosphere of an empty school play-ground.

We returned to the seat and continued down the old quarry path gently descending through woodland with some fine yew. The initial section of this path had been built-up on a **low wall**, now covered in moss. It then led steeply down to a stile that crossed over onto the track to

Whitbarrow Lodge. We turned right, along this track until we reached the road at Mill Side where we turned right again to follow the quiet country road to Beck Head. Where the road bears to the left, the 'beck' emerges from an undercut limestone cliff. Here we found maidenhair spleenwort and hart's tongue fern. The rocks by the emerging spring were covered in the liverwort *Conocephalum conicum* (its leaves smell of antiseptic when bruised). In the stream by the roadside were masses of watercress.

The road became a bridleway through a **tunnel of sycamore and ash**. We passed hedgerows full of the blue-flowering meadow cranesbill, past the unexpectedly-wild salad burnet. The bridleway joined the road to Witherslack Hall, which took us back to our starting point at the car park.

Taking it Further

The topography of this coastline was quite different after the last ice age. Morecambe Bay was thought to have extended north into the Winster valley as far as Coppy Beck (grid ref. SD427881) and into the Lyth valley to Underbarrow Pool (grid ref. SD467914). Whitbarrow would have been a sea cliff. The evidence comes from over 60 bore-holes sunk into the surrounding farmland. The analysis of the soil showed it to consist mostly of fine estuarine silts and sand.

The whole area north of Morecambe Bay has been described as a 'raised beach'. Nowhere does it vary more than 2.5 ft either side of 15ft OD (OD refers to a standard datum line). The eastern side of Whitbarrow would have overlooked 18 square miles of estuary. Today, this so-called 'fossil coastline' is represented by 15 square miles of raised beach.

There is no evidence of a wave-cut platform at the base of Whitbarrow, or of any notch at the foot of the cliff. However, there is evidence of wave attack on the more-exposed Winder Moor, west of Humphrey Head. Here the wave action of long ago has notched into the seaward-facing sides of drumlins at Holme, grid ref. SD377752 and Raven Winder, grid ref. SD360744 (see Gresswell 1958).

Bibliography

Cumbria RIGS booklet. Whitbarrow: a geological walk looking at rocks, plants and landscapes.

Greswell, R.K. (1958) The post-glacial raised beach in Furness and Lyth, North Morecambe Bay. *Institute of British Geographers Transactions and Papers* **25**: 79-103.

12. Fairfield – the Deerfence Mystery

Tracing Nab Scar's medieval walls.

Checklist:

Distance: 5.3 miles.

Ascent: 2000ft (600m).

Approximate Time: 4 to 5 hours.

Maps: 1:25 000 OS Explorer OL7. 1:50 000 OS Landranger 90. 1:50 000 British Geological Survey, England and Wales Sheet 38, Ambleside.

Terrain: Steep, resurfaced stony path on the ascent of Nab Scar. The descent to Alcock Tarn is indistinct on steep grass. From Alcock Tarn to Rydal, the paths are well-used along easy gradients.

Equipment and Books: Binoculars and compass.

Footwear: Boots.

Parking: Roadside space for a limited number of cars outside Rydal Church (NY365063). Alternatively: White Moss Common (NY351065).

Public Transport: Buses from Kendal to Windermere, Ambleside and Grasmere, Stagecoach Service 599.

Refreshments: Grasmere and Rydal.

Fairfield holds a secret. There are great views and a tremendous high-level ridge walk that has become a classic fell race known as 'The Fairfield Horseshoe'. I remember 30 years ago, starting from outside Rydal Hall with 150 other runners, crammed together, all jostling for position between stone walls, then breaking out to head directly up Nab Scar. Now, the newly-constructed path zigzags gently upwards, and the erosion from that earlier time has disappeared. But that wasn't the secret. It was time to revisit Fairfield and look for all those things I had missed when wearing running shoes. This was going to be Fairfield at one mile an hour.

And so I set off with friends with a new objective: to find a medieval deer fence that was built in 1277. I had read the archaeological report by Collingwood. I had seen a photograph in Millward and Robinson's book and in a publication by Winchester. No mention anywhere else – even Wainwright seemed to have passed this one by. The OS map indicated nothing except a line of modern cairns – bad news for a deer fence that was 800 years old.

We parked the car at the side of the lane by Rydal Church. We passed Rydal Mount and branched off left along the footpath to Nab Scar. We gradually gained height up what was now a stone staircase. I had the map. Mike had the food. Cath had the camera. But I also had an 'old map' – an OS second edition – that I kept to myself!

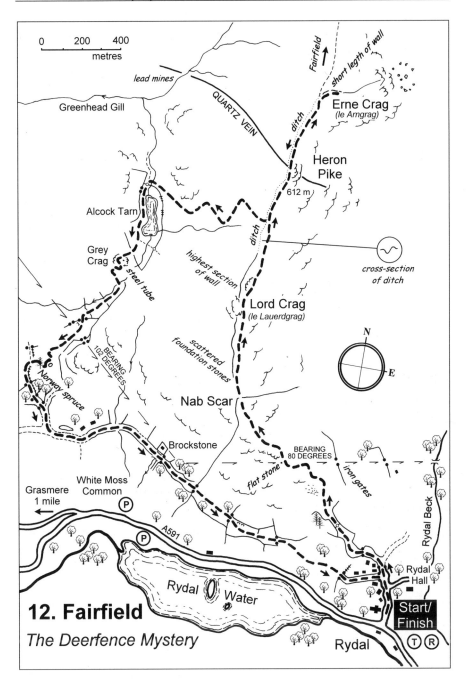

0 200 400
metres

lead mines

Greenhead Gill

QUARTZ VEIN

ditch

Fairfield

short legth of wall

Erne Crag
(le Arngrag)

Heron
Pike

612 m

Alcock Tarn

ditch

Grey
Crag

highest section
of wall

steel tube

cross-section
of ditch

Lord Crag
(le Lauerdgrag)

scattered
foundation stones

BEARING
102 DEGREES

Norway spruce

N

E

Nab Scar

Brockstone

White Moss
Common

Grasmere
1 mile

P

flat stone

BEARING
80 DEGREES

iron gates

Rydal Beck

A591

P

Rydal
Hall

Rydal
Water

12. Fairfield

The Deerfence Mystery

Rydal

Start/
Finish

T R

I took a quick glance at the 'old map'.

"We should see some **iron gates** somewhere down to the right."

We reached a prominent bend in the path that turned uphill sharply to the left. One hundred metres below us we could see a modern, iron gate, one metre wide with sandstone posts each side.

"There should be another about 400 metres further down."

And there it was, a second gate, identical to the first. The reason for the gates was shown only on the 'old map', and so when I took the compass bearing of 80 degrees along the line that linked the two gates, my companions were none the wiser.

We climbed until we reached the edge of Nab Scar's steep west side. The view was excellent. Looking across Rydal Water we could even see into the opening of Rydal Cave. Three metres back from the edge of the path there was a **flat stone**, one-metre square by about 20 centimetres thick. It had been placed here on the edge of the crags for no apparent reason. It had no carvings or identification marks. I stood on the block and took out the compass. Looking along the 80 degree bearing that had been previously set, the compass pointed directly to the second gate (the first gate was hidden from view). This meant that there was a straight line that began at the stone and ran exactly through both gates.

The block of stone was on the highest point of this imaginary line. Why? And what was the significance of the modern, iron gates with imported sandstone posts? And why were the gates padlocked? We climbed higher. The deer fence was the next mystery. The old map was of little help. All that I had was Collingwood's 1930 paper and he couldn't draw the fence on a map because nobody had been able to work out exactly where it went. The line taken by the fence was based on a manuscript written in Latin and French. Many of the place-names were no longer in use and their present-day equivalents could only be guessed at. The translation, however, was a fascinating account of a dispute between two neighbours. Roger de Lancaster owned the land that drained into Rydal Beck where he kept a deer park. William de Lyndesy owned the neighbouring land, and his tenants' livestock kept straying into the deer park. The course of action agreed by both parties was to share in the building of a fence to keep out the trespassing beasts. Roger was to build the first section, nearly three-quarters of a mile long, from his hunting lodge at *Rogerloge*; and William was to construct a section of equal length to reach *le Crag in le Grencoue* – which translates into 'the Crag in the Green Cove'.

None of the points can be drawn with certainty on a modern OS map.

Roger's Lodge is probably the hunting lodge shown at grid reference NY369055, but where is the Crag in the Green Cove? Intuition is all we have to go by, and Green Cove suggests a fertile hollow near water – most likely somewhere on the edge of Rydal Water.

The manuscript recalls how Roger was to build a high-level section that was to lead from Rydal Water up Nab Scar to *le Lauerdgrag* (Lord Crag) and William was to continue this with help from another neighbour, Margaret de Ros, to join up with *le Arngrag* (Erne Crag). All this was to be completed by Michaelmas, 1277.

We kept looking over the edge of Nab Scar for any sign, but the wall

leading up from Rydal Water looked to belong to a later century (it is thought to have been completed by 1581, see Winchester 2000a). We reached the top and passed through a gap in the wall. Twenty metres further, we found what we were looking for – a line of **scattered foundation stones** snaking across the ridge to the left of the path. Where a modern cairn had been built to mark the path, the old wall had been robbed out. The best-preserved sections were those furthest away from the cairns. Looking back to the summit of Nab Scar, there was no trace. The old wall had been 'recycled' to build the new wall.

On the ascent of Heron Pike, the deerfence changes from a stone wall to a ditch – marked by the line of rushes. The earth was thrown up on the Rydal side (right) to form a bank, probably surmounted by a post and wattle fence.

We walked on to

le Lauerdgrag. The wall became more impressive. The modern path deviated away from the craggy ridge to the right but the deer fence kept to its craggy line and here reached its maximum height of 0.7 metres.

Two hours had flown by. We had lunch just behind a vertical outcrop facing the **highest section of wall**. In two hours the leading fell-runners, with north-country accents, would have been home and dry. But ours was a medieval challenge – and we were speaking in French.

We left our picnic site and continued on to Erne Crag. Suddenly the wall stopped and the line of the deerfence continued as a **ditch**. The earth was thrown up on the Rydal side to form an embankment on top of which would probably have been built a post and wattle fence. This would have kept out the sheep and goats but allowed the free movement of deer. The ditch could be followed along a line that sometimes ran adjacent to and sometimes left of the path. Where the ground was level, the finely-eroded soil had filled-in the ditch, but with care the line could still be followed.

We reached Heron Pike with its vein of white quartz. This was the highest point reached by the deerfence – the responsibility of Margaret de Ros. Two hundred metres further, it was to veer off to the right to join the craggy outcrop of Erne Crag. This section was very difficult to trace, but after crossing the path, there was evidence that it ran up to the crags as a **short length of wall**.

Now we were left with a puzzle. The 1277 records refer to the deerfence ending on Erne Crag. It must have joined on to some pre-existing fence or wall but there is no record of where this might be. The obvious line was that taken by the modern fell wall (or 'head dyke') that cuts across the Rydal Valley to join up with and follow the ridge down over Low Pike and back to the hunting lodge. This modern wall was not completed until 1565 (see Winchester 2000a), but perhaps it was built over the line of the missing deerfence.

This was our furthest point on the Fairfield Horseshoe. We doubled back over Heron Pike. On its summit there are a number of narrow veins of quartz that mark a fault line. This leads west into Greenhead Gill where it has been mined for lead and zinc. Once over Heron Pike we dropped down to AlcockTarn. Although there is no path marked on the map, Wainwright shows this as a way down (Wainwright 1955). The route follows a fairly steep grassy slope but there are no problems with hidden crags. We eventually reached the north end of the tarn to join the footpath leading back to White Moss Common. The route took us gently down, zigzagging past Grey Crag, past a **steel tube** for erecting the flag pole to mark the highest point in the Grasmere Fell Race; on past the outflow stream of Alcock Tarn, through an area of mature larch and then through a gate, a seat and then ... another iron gate with sandstone posts.

The puzzle of the gates had returned. And if the pattern is repeated we should expect a second and then a third gate to follow a straight line. Further down the path on the left we spotted the second gate, and beyond that in the next wall, a third. I took the compass bearing. It read 102 degrees. The same padlocked gates were following a straight line, coming across from Thirlmere – more significantly, Thirlmere *Reservoir* [see 'Solutions' for the explanation].

The path dropped down through sheltered woodland that had been landscaped with hidden pools and overflow channels. We past a

What was the significance of the modern iron gates with imported sandstone posts? And why were the gates padlocked?

magnificent **Norway spruce** that would equal any in Trafalgar Square; down a trackway bordered with dense rhododendrons to emerge eventually onto the path linking Grasmere and Rydal. We followed a route that kept a fairly level course past hidden cottages. The path eventually led us back to the road and our starting point at the car.

Taking it Further

Earlier deer parks were much smaller in size, usually ranging from ten to one hundred acres and were primarily a source of meat. They were designed with a ditch facing inwards to stop the deer from getting out. The outer bank was typically fenced with oak stakes or planted with a thick hedge. The idea of keeping deer for sport developed later in the medieval period with the fencing off of much larger enclosures. Rydal provides an example of this change, and this is seen in the construction of the ditch and embankment on Heron Pike. The ditch was dug on the outside of the deer park to stop livestock such as cows, sheep and goats from getting in but would have been low enough to allow the free passage of deer. This type of fence was built around the head of Eskdale in the late 13th century by the monks of Furness Abbey. Unlike the Rydal fence, the boundary-line in Eskdale can be traced on modern OS 1: 25 000 maps. Look carefully along a line that follows the east bank of the River Esk starting at grid reference NY220054 and ending at NY234077. The intermittent black line shows the remaining turf walls.

The keeping of livestock led to a regulated system of land management. The 'head dykes' were built to separate the valleys from the open fell. These walls played a fundamental part in livestock control (see Winchester 2000b). The farming year was divided into the 'open season', when livestock were allowed below the head dyke, and the 'closed season', when they were kept out. The dates were traditionally taken from the Christian calendar and enforced by local courts. The closed season began on St Helen's Day (3rd May) and ended on either All Saints' Day (1st November) or Martinmas (11th November). However, some manor courts allowed the closed season to end at Michaelmas (24th September). This must have been the case at Rydal where the 1277 document refers to Michaelmas for completion of the deer fence. The significance of this date now becomes clear: the deer park had to be made stock-proof before the neighbouring animals were allowed back down into the surrounding valleys.

Bibliography

Collingwood, W.G (1930) The medieval fence of Rydal and other linear earthworks. *Transactions of the Cumberland and Westmorland Antiquary and Archaeological Society* **XXX** (New Series): 1-11.

Millward, R and Robinson, A. (1970) *The Lake District*: Illustration 23a. Eyre and Spottiswoode, London.

Wainwright, A.W. (1955) *A Pictorial Guide to the Lakeland Fells, Book One: The Eastern Fell*: Heron Pike, 2. Westmorland Gazette.

Winchester, A.J.L. (2000a) *The Harvest of the Hills*: 29. Edinburgh University Press.

Winchester, A.J.L. (2000b) *ibid.*: 55.

13. Dovedale – the Strange Case of the Twisted Trees

The effect of lead mines on the local ecology

Checklist:

Distance: 3 miles.

Ascent: 650ft (200m).

Approximate Time: 2 to 3 hours

Maps: 1:25 000 OS Explorer OL5. 1:50 000 OS Landranger 90. 1:50 000 British Geological Survey, England and Wales Sheet 29, Keswick.

Terrain: Mostly level or easy gradients and well-defined paths except for short section crossing Dovedale Beck to join the return footpath.

Equipment and Books: Wildflower guidebook.

Footwear: Boots.

Special Considerations: The twisted trees are in an advanced state of decay. Please keep to the footpath when passing through this area to minimise their disturbance.

Parking: Hotel car park for patrons only. Parking at Sykeside camp site on payment of a daily fee.

Public Transport: Buses from Bowness to Glenridding. Stagecoach Service 517 'The Kirkstone Rambler'.

Refreshments: Brothers Water Inn.

```
Chris,
Attached is a
spread-sheet with the
results. The section of
interest is the one
labelled 'metal
concentration in leaves'.
The units are in mgs of
metal/kg of dried leaves,
i.e. ppm.
A to H are your samples.
Sorry the lead results
are negative.
Let me know if you need
any more help.
Cheers,
Mark
```

I cast my eye over the E-mail and quickly opened the attached spread-sheet. The lead (Pb) results were disappointingly negative. There was no correlation with the degree of spiralling. But when I examined the results for calcium (Ca), it was a different story.

I cast my mind back three months to that day in April when I first collected the samples. I had known there was something strange about the birch in Dovedale from a previous visit and had sought permission from the National Trust to take samples. I had arranged with the Department of Soil Science at the University of Reading to have the samples analysed. All that was needed was for me to collect some leaves.

I left the car at the Brothers Water Inn where I was hoping to round off the day with a bar meal. I followed the farm track from the camp site over Kirkstone Beck. Before crossing the footbridge, I noticed the **hollow ash** on the right with an embedded iron hinge pin, causing the tree's tissue to grow around the intruder. Metals can do strange things to a tree's shape.

I continued on to Hartsop Hall and turned left. I past the sheep pens and cattle sheds and followed the level track alongside a **rocky knoll** covered in Scots pine. The quickest way to the twisted trees was the track up to the right, but I wanted to make a day of it, and explore some of Dovedale. I kept straight ahead.

The track followed the wall to a **barn** and then continued along a level grassy section at the side of Dovedale Beck. After crossing a plank footbridge, the path entered an area of tall bracken. All along this section were fine specimens of mature birch, alder and sycamore. The large **ant-hills** were some of the largest in the area, occupying the ground between the path and the beck. I checked the tops of some of the tallest for fox-droppings. After crossing a side stream, the path climbed a rocky section into a mossy clearing before reaching the beck. There was evidence that the flow had been dammed. On the opposite bank, a section of wall suggested the start of a canal or 'leat' that had redirected water to the lead mines lower down the valley.

The path now climbed gently alongside a series of waterfalls. Above the main fall, the beck split into two channels. The damp, still atmosphere of this section had caused many of the birch trees to become infected with white brackets of the **'razor-strop fungus'**. This was an enchanting spot where the beck took several detours, dividing and rejoining. It was here that I stumbled upon a delightful stone-slab footbridge crossing one of the tributaries. You could imagine trolls living here! Botanists would also enjoy this. I looked down at the boggy ground, full of star sedge and jointed rush, and found lousewort and butterwort.

Eventually the narrow grass path climbed gently through the bracken and led to a gate in the valley wall. A faint path ran above the south side of the beck. I reached a level area with a large **flat-topped boulder** where I crossed the beck. There was no obvious path here but as I climbed diagonally up the opposite bank I joined the path leading back down the valley.

The volcanic rock looked as though it has been scrambled and glued back together in a gravelly mixture of pebbles and fine grains. The result was a well-drained area, flushed through with a rich concentration of different minerals. The south-facing aspect provides ideal growing conditions and where the stream cut across the path, there was a variety of high-mountain plants. One area in particular, just across from the top gate, had yellow saxifrage, both types of lady's mantle, butterwort,

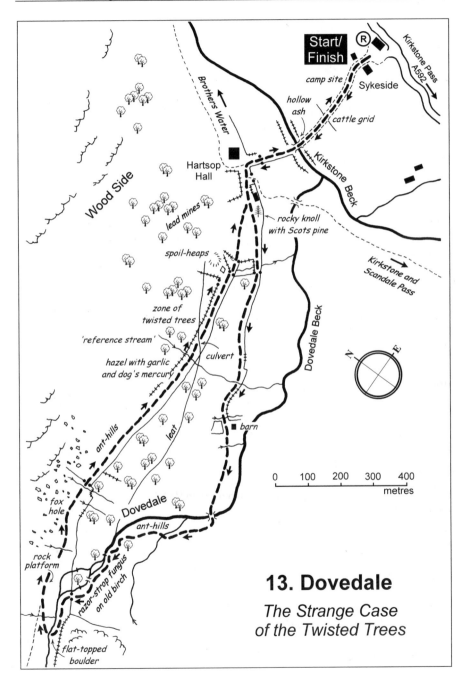

13. Dovedale

The Strange Case
of the Twisted Trees

sundew, scabious and harebells. Several metres further to the right of the path, I passed a **rock platform** that gave a fine view down the valley. This was as a look-out perch for the local crows. The last time I stood here, I found crows' pellets, and on this visit there were more pellets as well as black feathers.

The path continued dropping gently, following the line of the valley wall. I kept a careful watch on this wall, and opposite a gap filled with planks and wire, I stopped to look up the bank to my left. Here was one of the many boulders that litter this valley side, but this one had a **fox-hole** underneath with freshly-excavated soil.

After crossing a stream, I passed through a gate into an area with scattered hawthorn. The warm, 45 degree slope on this side of the valley had favoured the development of unusually large **ant-hills**. The path now followed the wall closely. After a stand of tall bracken, it led into a grove of hazel. The ground below was covered in split hazelnuts left by feeding squirrels. Along the side of the wall were lush growths of **garlic** and dog's mercury with wild arum hidden in between. All around were flowers that were normally found on limestone – primrose, dog violet, herb robert, wild strawberry and yellow pimpernel. I crossed a stream. This was an important reference point (it may help to call this the '**reference stream**'). Now things were about to get interesting, for I knew I was approaching the twisted trees. They occupied a zone, 40 metres wide that began at the stream and extended east across the valley slope.

It was six months ago that I first noticed that some of the downy birch had developed an anti-clockwise spiral, a corkscrew-like twist in their main trunk and side branches. My first thought was that it was the lead from the nearby lead mines which was affecting the trees' growth. There was also the complication that many of the plants growing in this area are what botanists call 'calcicoles' – plants found where there are high levels of calcium in the soil. The veins of lead were accompanied by quartz and secondary minerals that were leaching out into the soil. It was this that was producing the flush of 'lime-loving' plantlife such as the garlic and dog's mercury.

I selected my trees and collected approximately 20 leaves from each. I noted the position of each tree, noted the degree of spiralling, and photographed it. I collected the leaves and sealed them in a labelled polythene bag. I repeated this procedure for each of my eight sample trees.

Fifty metres past the reference stream, I noticed a stone-lined tunnel, or **culvert**, about 0.5 metres wide, emerging from below the wall. It ran diagonally down the path and crossed under the wire fence on my left.

'Spiralling' in downy birch (Sample A)

This was the water channel that had begun below the waterfalls in Dovedale Beck. As I continued my descent, the fellside on my left opened out to reveal the mine workings. The huge **spoil-heaps** were mostly bare of vegetation due to erosion of the scree-like surface and the toxic effects of the metals. And yet there was some re-colonisation, mostly by moss (*Polytrichum piliferum*) and by carline thistles – a plant more at home on limestone pavements.

This was an old mine even by Lake District standards. Records date back to 1696 and operations continued intermittently for over 200 years. There were, however, problems with obtaining sufficient water to power the machinery – hence the construction of the leat. Problems also arose when lead got into the local watercourses and poisoned fish and live-stock (Adams 1995). Was the lead also responsible for the twisted trees? I headed back down the path to rejoin the farm track by the knoll of Scots pine. From here I retraced my route back to the Brothers Water Inn and the stir-fried duck.

That was back in April. Now it was June and I had the results. I tele-phoned Mark:

"Thanks for the E-mail and for sending the results."

"Sorry they are negative." he replied.

"No, not at all! They are what they are."

It had been a fascinating whodunnit, but *the Case of the Twisted Trees* could now be filed away.

So, who put the twists in the Dovedale trees? Like all good detective stories, there has to be a villain … I guess we'll just have to say: "The calcium did it!"

Taking it Further

The samples were labelled A-H (double blind), and sent for independent identification. They were analysed for lead (Pb) and calcium (Ca) using an atomic absorption spectrophotometer. The results are shown in Figure 13.1.

Sample	A	B	C	D	E	F	G	H	Control
Calcium	12188.6	8798.4	8730.5	10632.3	7175.0	7069.0	5624.9	6998.3	14734.3
Lead	zero	1.7	0.1	zero	0.1	zero	0.9	3.2	5.0

(Laboratory Control – Spinach grown in contaminated soil of known lead content)

Figure 13.1 Concentration of metals in birch leaves (mg/kg)

Spiralling was assessed as:

❖ 'extreme' – a distinct wavy-edge to the profile of the trunk or branch.

❖ 'slight' – no distinct wavy profile, but spiralling still evident.

❖ 'none'.

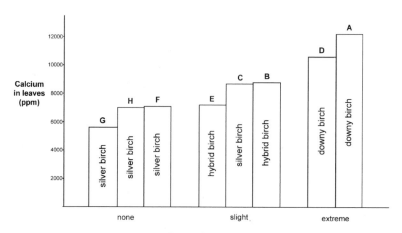

Figure 13.2 The relationship of 'spiralling' in birch to the concentration of calcium in leaves (samples A to H)

Downy birch (*Betula pubescens*) and silver birch (*B. pendula*) can be difficult to separate (Halliday 1997). There is the added complication that they can hybridise (Williamson 1989). Downy birch is usually found on acid soils with low calcium levels whilst silver birch is more at home on limestone. Both species are present in Dovedale. Although both exhibit spiralling, the silver birch is the least affected and would seem to be able to resist the uptake of calcium from the soil into its tissues. This ability to 'keep out calcium' may not exist in downy birch, which develops extreme spiralling in response to its high calcium uptake (see figure 13.2).

The experimental design of this pilot study could be improved: more samples; a more-objective measure of spiralling; more controls, including some non-spiralling downy birch. Despite these shortfalls, the results suggest that calcium uptake may have an important effect on the growth and form of downy and silver birch. However, until further surveys are undertaken, a genetic component of spiralling cannot be ruled out.

Bibliography

Adams, J. (1995) *Mines of the Lake District Fells*: 135-137, Dalesman Publications.

Halliday, G. (1997) *A Flora of Cumbria*: 140, University of Lancaster.

Williamson, S. (1989) *Betula pubescens* and *B. pendula* in Cumbria. Unpublished undergraduate dissertation, University of Lancaster.

14. Hallin Fell – the Riddle of Kailpot Crag

Discovering the geology and wildlife of Ullswater's eastern shoreline

Checklist:

Distance: 2.5 miles.

Ascent: 425ft (130m). Descent through Hallinhag Wood: 300ft (90m).

Approximate Time: Allow 2½ hours.

Maps: 1:25 000 OS Explorer OL5. 1:50 000 OS Landranger 90. 1: 250 000 British Geological Survey 54N 04W, Lake District.

Terrain: Mostly easy or level paths. The decent to the shoreline through Hallinhag Wood is steep across eroded soil with exposed tree roots.

Equipment and Books: Hand lens. Fungus identification guide.

Footwear: Boots.

Special Considerations: The start of the little-used path across the west side of Hallin Fell can easily be missed in late summer when the bracken has developed.

Parking: Roadside parking opposite St Peter's Church (NY435192).

Public Transport: Buses from Penrith via Pooley Bridge to Howtown, Stagecoach Service 109. The Royal Mail Postbus, Service 110 visits Martindale Hause.

When it comes to Hallin Fell, I have been as guilty as the next person – always rushing along the lakeside path to link up with the 'steamer'; or, if I've had a spare hour, rushing up to the memorial on the summit to steal the view. See everything and miss the detail.

The average walking speed in hill country is usually taken from Naismith's formula: three miles per hour plus an hour added for every 1500ft of ascent. But to see things, to *really* see things, you need to be moving slowly. At three miles per hour fellwalking is a physical exercise: at one mile per hour it becomes forensic science! And so it was, one fine October morning that I set out to see what I had been missing.

My starting point was St Peter's Church at the top of all the hairpins. I crossed the road and followed the path over the grass to a gate in a wall (signpost: public footpath). I crossed a field to the next stile (note the orienteering marker at its base) and crossed another field. The path led to a gate followed by a descent down a short flight of stone steps. At this point a clear path headed straight ahead towards Hallin Bank. The path I wanted turned up the gentle slope to my right, following the wall. This route seemed hardly used for it was almost completely hidden in tall bracken. In front of me was the corner of an enclosure with a plantation of young larch and mature Scots pine. The path followed the wall along the western flank of Hallin Fell. I was about to cross **four shallow streams** that began life as springs higher up the slope. By Lakeland standards, they should barely be worth a mention, but here on Hallin Fell, such surface water is unusual. There are, in fact, no major river systems associated with this fell – only a scattering of springs that have developed on the south and west-facing sides. Despite their small size, these watercourses had changed the pattern of vegetation. They were the only areas on the lower slope that was clear of bracken, and where they crossed the path, there were patches of jointed rush, marsh thistle and marsh pennywort.

The path continued following the wall and eventually began to descend gently towards Hallinhag Wood. Before entering the gate, I stopped to examine a rotting **oak branch** lying on the ground. Its surface was covered in the grey-green matchstick-sized stalks of *Cladonia coniocraea* – a lichen often found on rotting oak and on other trees with acid bark. Once inside the wood, the path dropped steeply between exposed tree roots. Early in the summer, the wood sorrel is in flower, and in this part of the wood they have pronounced purple veins spreading through the white petals.

At the bottom of the slope, I reached the busy shoreline path. Four hundred metres further and I was level with a rocky promontory jutting out into the lake. A narrow path led down through the bilberries and heather to the water's edge. I passed a two-metre-high birch stump on the right with large white brackets of the razor-strop fungus (*Piptoporus betulinus*). After only 30 metres, I was at the shoreline. The first things I noticed were the holes in the rocks. I counted ten that had been neatly drilled out. They were one-inch in diameter and were scattered in a seemingly random pattern... and then I found signs of an otter. It was on the rock on the left as I faced the lake, the one that juts out the furthest. Everything was perfect – an isolated bare rock surrounded by deep water, away from the trees and so with unrestricted views of any incoming danger. It was the patch of green algae, about the size of a saucer, that first caught my eye. With a hand lens I carefully examined its surface. Nothing! I was about to give up, and then in one of the rock cracks I spotted a single fish scale – enough to confirm an **otter** 'sprainting site'.

A few metres further east, there were two rocky bulges in the shoreline. These were not as isolated as the one just examined and had no tell-tale green algae. Instead, they were covered in *Hypnum*

Otter swimming in late evening light. These elusive animals were once a common sight along Ullswater's shoreline.

cupressiforme, a moss often found growing on acidic surfaces. On top of the moss were scattered 'pellets' from an unidentified bird – one that had been eating water beetles. What makes one rock suitable for otters and the other suitable for birds? Isolation? Water depth? Thirty metres away was one of the busiest paths in the Lake District. The key would seem to be the ability to escape quickly from an approaching threat.

In the 18th century, otters were common on Ullswater. An account by William Hutchinson in 1794 describes an otter hunt along this shoreline using dogs and a rowing boat. The description is completely matter-of-fact. No sentimentality was expressed, for otters in those days were regarded as vermin.

I left the site and returned to the main path. I continued past a sheltered grove of ash saplings and a huge sycamore, after which the path dropped down to a level section with a number of mature oaks. Two Scots pines occupied the low knoll on my left. Just beyond this, a narrow path led off to a shingle bay. I examined the rocks along the water's edge for green algae but found only the acid-loving moss. A careful search of the moss revealed more **bird 'pellets'**.

After a further 200 metres, the path opened out into an area of mature

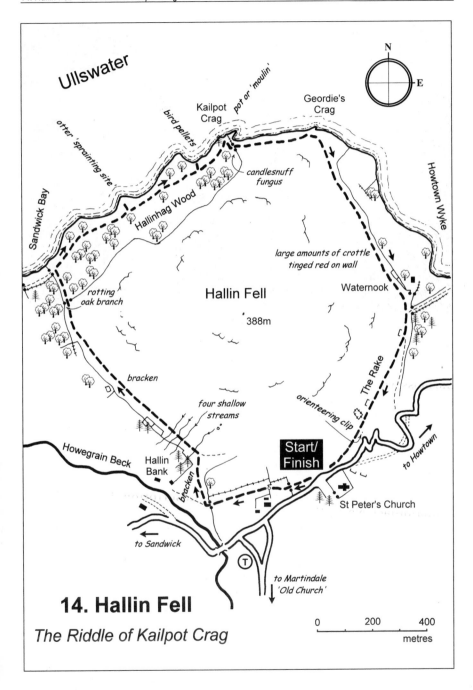

Ullswater

Kailpot Crag

pot or 'moulin'

bird pellets

otter 'sprainting site

Sandwick Bay

candlesnuff fungus

Hallinhag Wood

Geordie's Crag

Howtown Wyke

large amounts of crottle tinged red on wall

Waternook

rotting oak branch

Hallin Fell

388m

bracken

four shallow streams

The Rake

orienteering clip

Howegrain Beck

Hallin Bank

bracken

Start/ Finish

to Howtown

St Peter's Church

to Sandwick

to Martindale 'Old Church'

14. Hallin Fell

The Riddle of Kailpot Crag

0   200   400

metres

A view of Ullswater from the top of Kailpot Crag

beech. The rocky outcrop of Kailpot Crag with its Scots pine provided an almost theatrical backdrop. I climbed up the smooth sides and had lunch on the top.

Kailpot Crag has many interesting features. It is composed of basalt lava that has been scoured by ice. In the Lake District, glaciers generally moved from the high central ground towards the edge. The Ullswater glacier would have moved in a north-easterly direction towards Penrith, scouring the rock surfaces and over-deepening the lake. The resistant outcrops such as Kailpot Crag show signs of this movement, leaving a shape that slopes gently down where the ice rode over the surface and falls more steeply away on the lee side. Such a rock is called a *roche moutonée* because it is thought to resemble a wig – a *moutonée* – a French wig made of fleece. But an error in translation led it to be linked with the word *moutonière* meaning sheep-like. As with Cinderella's 'glass/fur' slipper – the error is somehow better. 'Stone sheep' seem more appropriate than 'stone wigs'!

There is also the puzzle of the 'Kailpot' itself. To see this feature, I had to stand on the top, five metres to the west of the boundary fence. By peering over the edge I could see a semicircular ledge about a metre out and just below the water surface. Over this ledge was a deep hollow or 'pot'. It is not known for certain how this was formed. It may be the regular grinding effect of loose stones moved by wave action around the rocky promontory. But a more-likely explanation goes back to the time when the wet ice covering this area was breached by a flow of melt-water from a glacial stream. The water flowed in circular eddies at this point and eroded the bedrock below. Such a feature is known as a *moulin*, from the French for 'windmill'.

All this is far from the minds of the hapless Outward Bound students waiting their turn to jump in. Unlike Eskdale, where students are required to jump off a bridge into a river, here at Ullswater, they jump off the top of the crag into the 'pot'.

On the top of the crag, were the letters 'KC' painted on one of the vertical sides. Around the letters were more of the one-inch-diameter drill holes arranged in a random cluster. At first I thought it was something to do with the Outward Bound Centre – anchor points for mooring a boat or for abseiling? Then I thought it was something to do with the geology and so I looked more closely at the geology map. It showed a miniature compass arrow printed opposite the crag, together with the number '33'. The legend at the side of the map read as follows: 'Mean direction of the stable natural remnant magnetization relative to local bedding.' Mmm ..., but what about the holes? [see 'Taking it Further' for a translation!]

After visiting the crag I wondered across to examine an old beech that had been felled and sawn into logs. It was next to the fence, several metres to the right of the gate. At the edge of the bark on one of the logs I found the appropriately-named **'candle-snuff fungus'** (*Xylaria hypoxylon*). It had black stalks about two centimetres long, with pale grey tips. A much larger fungus was growing at ground-level between the roots of the sawn-off tree base. This was the bracket fungus *Ganoderma applanatum* which causes 'heart rot', particularly in over-mature beech. This would undoubtedly have killed the tree.

I rejoined the path and continued through the gate leading out of the wood. The path led around the base of the open fell with extensive slopes of bracken over to the right. After passing the basalt promontory of Geordie's Crag, the path swung south and followed an old stone wall. Most Lakeland walls in sheltered sites have a covering of **'crottle'** (*Parmelia saxatilis*), but on this wall it was particularly luxuriant. Most of the colonies were tinged red – an effect normally confined to bird-perching sites, but here it could be found along the whole length of the wall. Perhaps it was something in the rock? Much of the basalt lava in this area was tinged red with iron oxides.

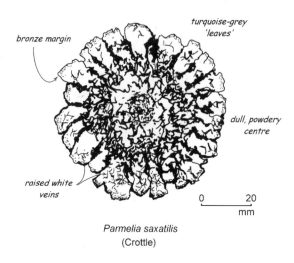

bronze margin

turquoise-grey
'leaves'

dull, powdery
centre

raised white
veins

0   20
mm

Parmelia saxatilis
(Crottle)

Figure 14.1 A rosette-shaped colony of crottle (*Parmelia saxatilis*) growing on the wall to the east of Hallin Fell. Normally the 'leaves' are turquoise-grey, but here they are tinged red.

On reaching a seat, the path branched down to the left but I kept straight ahead along 'The Rake'. From here I had an aerial view of the road with its hairpin bends. The original 'road' could be seen as a grassed-over track taking a more direct line of ascent. After passing another seat, a fenced-off spring, and then an orienteering checkpoint – I reached the road that took me back to my starting point.

Taking it Further

The drill holes along this part of Ullswater's shoreline provided core samples to determine the earth's magnetic history. Combining data from these and many other sites, it is possible to work out the position of the Lake District on the Earth's crust through geological time. The basalt lavas erupted at high temperatures and when they cooled they acquired what geologists call a magnetic signature. This 'remnant magnetization' reflects their orientation within the Earth's magnetic field that was present at the time of their eruption, 450 million years ago.

Bibliography

Hutchinson, W. (1794-1797) *The History of the County of Cumberland*, **I**: 448. Jollie, Carlisle. Republished by EP Publishing Ltd. In collaboration with Cumberland County Library (1974).

15. Haweswater – a Calculation at High Loup

Using lichens to find the age of Mardale's abandoned ruins

Checklist:

Distance: 5.5 miles.

Ascent: 1640ft (500m).

Approximate Time: 5 hours.

Maps: 1:25 000 OS Explorer OL5. 1:50 000 OS Landranger 90.

Terrain: Mostly dry well-defined paths. The section after leaving the Corpse Road, from Selside End to Selside Pike, is less clear and requires care in mist.

Equipment and Books: Compass, ruler, hand lens, binoculars.

Footwear: Boots.

Special Considerations: Please take care to avoid dislodging any stonework in the ruined buildings at High Loup. Some of the walls are leaning and in a dangerous condition.

Parking: Car park at Mardale Head (NY469107).

Public Transport: None.

Refreshments: Haweswater Hotel.

We were visiting the north-east corner of the Lake District and had allowed ourselves half a day to draw some lichen growth curves – a plot of the diameters of the largest lichens against the dates of gravestones on which they grow. The churchyards had to be as close as possible to Haweswater. We drove along the old A6 to Shap. Two hours later we had 25 points on a growth curve. The next planned stop was at St Michael's Church in Barton, where we plotted a further 44 points. Now we were ready for Haweswater.

The reason for all this frantic preparation was to try and put some dates to a group of ruined buildings that were positioned around the Mardale Corpse Road in an area called High Loup. No one had been able to date these buildings or even come up with a satisfactory explanation as to why they were built (see Lancaster University Archaeology Unit Surveys 1997-1998).

We arrived at the Mardale Head car park armed with compass, note pad and ruler. Most important of all, we had the growth curves. But this was an exposed valley rather than a sheltered churchyard and so I needed to check their accuracy for this area. We wandered a short distance back down the road and measured 20 of the largest colonies of map lichen (*Rhizocarpon geographicum*) on the roadside wall. The wall was built between 1937 and 1940, before the completion of the dam in

Model of Mardale church kept in the Haweswater Hotel
♀ The church was demolished when the reservoir was built, but parts of the building were incorporated into other structures. See if you can spot *where* exactly, in the accompanying photographs. [see 'Solutions']

1941. The average lichen diameter was 60 mm which gave a date of 1934 from the graph. That was good enough.

Whilst everyone was heading up Gatesgarth or Nan Bield Pass, or along to Riggindale to see the eagles, we took the shoreline path below the road. Across the lake we could see the wooded slope of The Rigg. Just out from where the trees begin, below the water surface, were the ruins of the 17th-century farmstead of Brackenhowe. Here had lived the Holme family, one of the first inhabitants of Mardale. The path led us above a **curved bay** with layers of silt

Post-box set in the wall outside Haweswater Hotel

and stones graded into parallel bands caused by wave action. Just below this bay had stood the old Dun Bull Inn. That was before this bay was formed – as far back as 1829 – when the Jacksons, Haytons and Clarkes knew it as their local hostelry. The adjacent farm was known as 'The Fold'. Its water supply came from a **spring** which is still running strongly across the path.

Further along, we

Draw-off tower on east side of Haweswater

reached the site of Grove Brae with its planted larch. In 1706 it was known as Grove Brake reflecting the extensive growth of bracken in this sheltered corner. The house was still occupied in 1938. Today, only the broken field walls show above the water with a few scattered larch, ash and oak. We climbed up towards the new road, above the submerged ruins of Goosemire. Now we could sense the history of this place even more, for we were about to join the Corpse Road.

The roadside signpost says: "Public Footpath Old Corpse Road Swindale." As we climbed the first zigzag, we looked back across Haweswater to the flooded village. The route we were on would have started outside The Holy Trinity Church. You can see the spot, 20 metres out from the end of The Rigg, tucked below the island of Wood Howe. There are records of a wedding held here in 1586 but there was no grave-yard until 1728. Up until then, residents had to carry their dead over to St Michael's Church at Shap, first crossing Chapel Bridge (still intact below the water) and then Arnold Bridge (now demolished).

The initial set of zigzags is surprisingly steep and the fellside was appropriately named 'Resting Hows'. The next zigzag to the right passes Low Loup with magnificent views of the tree-lined waterfalls in Rowantreethwaite Beck – but too far away for refreshment. And then we

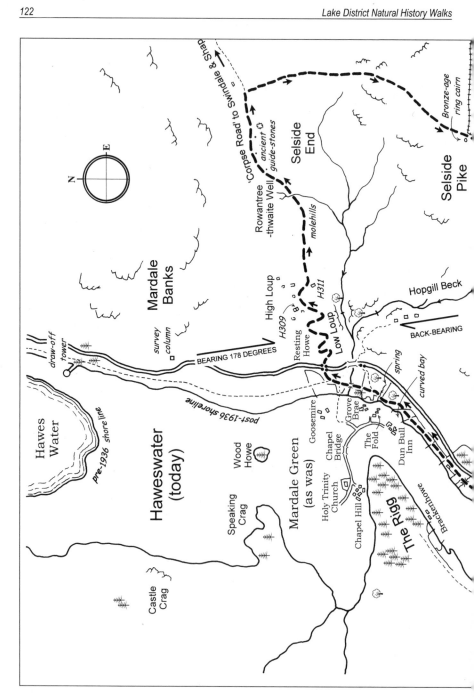

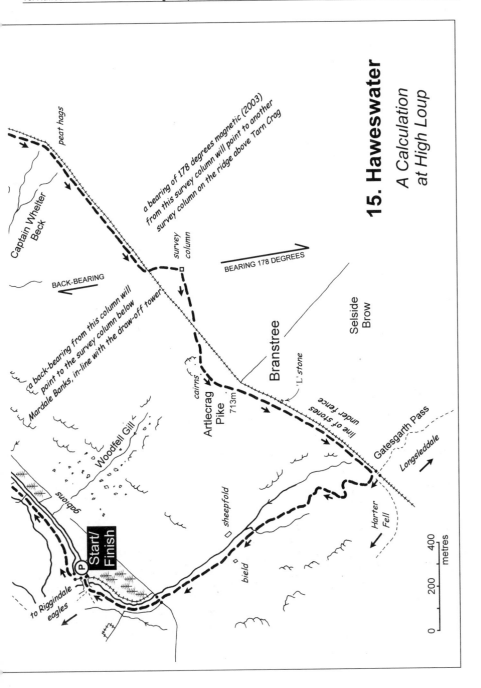

15. Haweswater

A Calculation at High Loup

BEARING 178 DEGREES

a bearing of 178 degrees magnetic (2003) from this survey column will point to another survey column on the ridge above Tarn Crag

survey column

BACK-BEARING

a back-bearing from this column will point to the survey column below Mardale Banks, in-line with the draw-off tower

peat hags

Captain Whelter Beck

Woodfell Gill

Artlecrag Pike 713m

cairns

Branstree

'L' stone

line of stones under fence

Selside Brow

Gatesgarth Pass

Longsleddale

Harter Fell

sheepfold

bield

Start/ Finish

to Riggindale eagles

0   200   400
metres

reached the top-most zigzag at High Loup. The last time a funeral party came this way was in 1736. What would they have seen at High Loup? – Cattle bields? Walled enclosures? Summer shielings or peat scales? Most are now in ruins but there are two substantial buildings with evidence of slate roofs.

Our intention was to apply the techniques of lichenometry to this archaeological puzzle (see 'Taking it Further'). All the buildings at High Loup have been given numbers based on a Lancaster University Survey in 1997. The first substantial building is **H309**. It has two rooms; that to the north having been added on later (you can tell this by examining the stonework outside the west wall). We measured the diameters of the largest colonies of map lichen that we could find. The next significant building is **H311**: a single room with two windows and a lintel still intact over the doorway. Once again we measured the largest map lichens. We had the growth curves from Shap and Barton taken earlier that day, together with growth curves from Crosthwaite and the Vale of St John taken from a previous study (Winchester 1988). Could these provide some useful dates?

Building H311 at High Loup. Could the lichens give the date when it was built and when it lost its roof?

It soon became clear that the growth curves could not help determine when the buildings were erected. The large size of the lichens on the outside walls fell outside the accuracy range of the graph. But those lichens on the inside walls were consistently smaller and fell well within the graph's range.

Why should the colonies be smaller on the inside walls? The answer was the roof, or the lack of it. Lichens require light and moisture and those on the inside have only been growing since the roofs collapsed. More significantly – their size indicates *when* the roofs collapsed. I read the figures from the graph (see Figure 15.1). H309 lost its roof in 1929; its extension lost its roof in 1958, and H311 lost its roof in 1945 (assuming an accuracy of plus or minus five years). But that leaves us with a problem. These were heavy roofs – one slate inside the entrance of H309 measures 920mm x 52mm x 2.5mm. To support such a weight there would have to have been substantial roof timbers. And yet no sign of

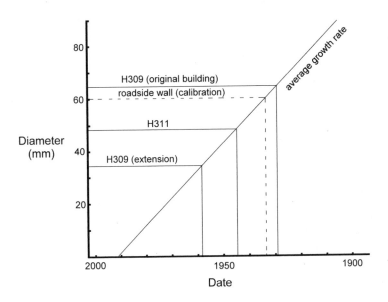

Figure 15.1 The average growth rate of map lichen (*Rhizocarpon* sp.) in north-east Cumbria. Data collected from St Mary's Church (Crosthwaite), Keswick; Vale of St John's Church, near Threlkeld; St Michael's Church, Shap; St Michael's Church, Barton. The Haweswater wall was built between 1937-1940, which suggests an accuracy of plus or minus 5 years for this region of the graph. The largest lichen diameters from the inside walls of H309 and H311 can be used to read-off the dates when the roofs collapsed. (Data for Crosthwaite and Vale of St John supplied by Vanessa Winchester.)

wood remains, inside or out. If the lichenometry is correct, there would not have been sufficient time for the timber to have decayed.

Perhaps the biggest puzzle of all is 'Why were they built?' If this were Eskdale, they would most likely have been peat huts where semi-dried peat was stored on its way down to the valley. But these buildings at High Loup have windows, suggesting that they may have been used as temporary accommodation or shielings, when cattle was brought up to graze on Mardale Common.

We sat and had our lunch inside H309. It was noticeable how the lichens changed from wall to wall. The south-facing wall had large amounts of map lichen from about one metre upwards, indicating its exposure to sunlight. The north-facing wall was quite different with a scattering of rust-coloured lichens. (Whilst having lunch, see if you can spot a tiny rust-red mite on these lichens. A hand lens is essential as these creatures are less than 0.2mm long!)

Lunch over, we set off once again along the Corpse Road. Since the beginning of our climb, there had been no nearby streams to drink from. Now we reached the source of Rowantreethwaite Beck. Its importance for travellers was shown on the map. It is accorded its own name: 'Rowantreethwaite Well'. The site was marked on the ground by an ancient cairn at the side of the path. This must have been an important refreshment stop for funeral parties.

The route now climbed higher across the northern flank of Selside End. Modern cairns had been built, some with wooden poles, to help navigate this section in thick mist or drifting snow. Our funeral party back in 1736 would have followed three **ancient guide stones**. The permanence and age of two of these stones was shown by their yellow tops.

Two-hundred metres past the third guide stone, we reached the highest point on the Corpse Road marked by a wooden post. Our route now diverged south along a faint grassy path onto Selside End. (In mist this section could be difficult to follow unless you are proficient with a map and compass.). On this fine September day, we reached a rocky outcrop several metres below the summit of Selside. From here we had magnificent views down into Swindale. A large cairn crowns the summit of Selside. The word 'Cairn' is written in italics on the OS maps indicating something of antiquity rather than a modern artefact. It is a Scheduled Ancient Monument – a **Bronze Age ring cairn** – but many of its stones have been used to build a modern shelter at its centre. The original stonework can still be seen forming a raised kerb around its edge.

We continued along a more distinct path keeping the fence to our left. After a boggy section through eroded peat hags at the head of Captain Whelter Beck, the path climbed very gently with fine views west across to Kidsty Pike and east to Shap. A gentle descent took us down to the depression that feeds Hopegill Beck. From here we could see a tall **survey column** against the skyline to our left. On the 1:25 000 OS map this is marked 'Pillar'. It is worth studying the map carefully for there are several 'Pillars' in this area between Haweswater and Longsleddale. One can be found on Mardale Banks, grid reference NY480126. The second is the one on the skyline at NY484103; a third on the ridge of Tarn Crag at NY488078. Two more can be found at the head of Longsleddale at NY490064 and NY491062. If you place a ruler on the map, all five are connected by a straight line! What's more, the line leads directly to the draw-off tower on the east shore of Haweswater. The Pillars were built in 1926, to survey the line of the aqueduct taking water to Manchester, via Longsleddale and Kendal. It is worth a detour to visit the one on the skyline. From here, take a back-bearing of 178 degrees and site the line northwards towards Mardale Banks. With binoculars you should see the first pillar silhouetted against Haweswater. Now site the line in the opposite direction along the same bearing and you will see the third pillar, one and a half miles distant, on top of the ridge at Tarn Crag.

We crossed Artlecrag Pike with its two well-built **cairns**. The Borrowdale Volcanic rock found here has cleaved into many fine slabs that are perfect for building cairns. Strange, therefore, that there is no Ordnance Survey column – only a trig point set in the ground surrounded by what looks like a concrete 'Polo Mint'.

Now it was downhill all the way to the top of Gatesgarth Pass, following the line of a wire fence across the broad shoulder of Branstree. After approximately 200 metres from the summit, we came across a stone slab set upright against the wire. On its surface was a perfectly carved letter **'L'** – upper case, Times Roman, neatly incised into the stone. 'L' for 50? On the other side was carved the letter 'H'. Underneath the bottom wire was another mystery: an ancient line of stones, giving the impression that someone in the past had started to build a wall and had given up at the level of the foundations. An interesting puzzle, that became clear on studying the OS 1:25 000 map [see 'Solutions' if you haven't already spotted the evidence from the map.]

Further along the fence, I couldn't help noticing the reef knots – tied in the wire. And then it was Gatesgarth Pass – well-trodden ground for the first time on this entire walk. The path lead us gently down without difficulty to the car park.

Taking it Further

Before getting involved in lichenometry, it is important to appreciate its limitations. Ideally, lichens grow in circular colonies. The older the surface: the larger the colony. The problems start when we wish to fit accurate dates to the process. If we already know the date of a surface, and measure its largest colony, we can plot this on a graph; and if we have a range of dates we can plot a growth curve.

In lichenometry, gravestones often provide the dates: *Rhizocarpon geographicum* provides the measurements. With a suitable growth curve from as close to the study area as possible, we can work backwards: measuring the largest colony on the surface to be dated and reading off the age directly from the graph. There are many limitations. We cannot say for certain that a surface is 50 years old, only that it is *at least* 50 years old. But that may be better than nothing.

Most groups of cells, whether in the form of a complex organism or a yeast culture, exhibit a sigmoid growth curve: a slow start (lag phase) followed by accelerated growth (logarithmic phase) and ending with a stationary phase and death. This characteristic growth pattern is due in part to the problem of transporting metabolites across increasingly longer distances. *R. geographicum* is unusual in exhibiting a linear growth 'curve'. This is thought to be due to its cells growing within autonomous areas (areoli), freeing it from the problems of transporting carbohydrates etc. across the colony as a whole (see Innes 1985).

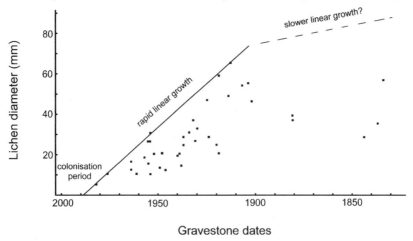

Figure 15.2 Growth 'curve' of *Rhizocarpon geographicum* at St Michael's Church, Barton. The initial growth rate is linear. Lichen growth is depicted as an 'envelope curve' enclosing the largest diameter colonies.

Linear growth is ideal for lichenometry (life is complex enough!). The simple, straight line represents a constant growth rate which in *R. geographicum* can last for up to 120 years. After this so-called 'great period', slower growth occurs which is more difficult to assess (see Figure 15.2). In Britain, lichen growth rates are highest in the west due to the higher rainfall. For *R.. geographicum*, values of 1.47mm per year have been recorded in North Wales (Winchester and Chaujar 2002) whilst 0.09 is more often found on the east coast of Scotland (Topham 1977). It is remarkable that the growth rates within the study area in Cumbria are in such close agreement: 1.25mm per year at Keswick (NY445912); 1.18mm at Threlkeld (NY306225); 1.05mm at Shap (NY564154) and 0.85 mm per year at Barton (NY487264). This gives an average of 1.08mm per year. For practical purposes, this average growth rate was here considered valid for this part of Cumbria. Lichen measurements taken from the Haweswater roadside wall (built between 1937 and 1940) confirmed this.

Support for the results also comes from cartographic evidence. The OS 1:10 000 maps distinguish between buildings with and without roofs. The first edition map was surveyed in 1858 and shows H309 and H311 with roofs intact, The second edition map was surveyed in 1915 but unfortunately it does not show clearly whether the roofs were still there. However, it does show that an additional room had been added on to the north side of H309: strong circumstantial evidence that both roofs were still intact in 1915.

(One final point on the lichenometry – the growth curves are based on measurements of colonies found on the backs of gravestones, almost all of which are vertical west-facing surfaces. When measuring colonies on other surfaces, these should also be vertical and west-facing.)

The rust-coloured lichen observed over lunch in H309 was *Opegrapha gyrocarpa*. This belongs to a group of lichens that form a characteristic 'alliance' associated with north-facing, silica-rich stonework (see James *et al*. 1977). A close examination of this rust-coloured surface with a x10 hand lens may reveal rust-coloured mites of the family Camerobiidae. They have eight legs and are less than 0.2 mm long. The active larval stage has only six legs and is even smaller. Their colour matches the lichen perfectly. Why? Is it diet? Is there some evolutionary selection taking place favouring those that are camouflaged?

Rare Camerobiid mites found on the north-facing walls at High Loup. These predatory mites match the colour of the rust-coloured lichens. This photomacrograph shows an adult with eight legs and an active larva with six legs.

Bibliography

Hopkins, B (1990) Mardale. _Unpublished typescript_, SMR 6847. Cumbria Sites and Monuments Record, County Offices, Kendal.

Innes, J.L. (1985) Lichenometry. _Progress in Physical Geography_ **9** (2): 187-254.

James, P.W., Hawkesworth, D.L. and Rose, F. (1977) Lichen communities in the British Isles: a preliminary conspectus. In _Lichen Ecology_ (M.R.D. Seaward, ed.): 295-413. Academic Press, London.

Lancaster University Archaeology Unit (1997) Haweswater Estate Archaeology Survey, _Phase 3_: 69-71.

Lancaster University Archaeology Unit (1998) Haweswater Estate, Detail Survey Report. _Report no.1998-1999/AUA7789/012_.

Topham, P.B. (1997) Colonisation, growth, succession and competition. In _Lichen Ecology_ (M.R.D. Seaward, ed.): 31-68. Academic Press, London.

Winchester, A.J.L. (2000) _The Harvest of the Hills_: 29. Edinburgh University Press.

Winchester, V. (1988) An assessment of lichenometry as a method for dating recent stone movements in two stone circles in Cumbria and Oxfordshire. *Botanical Journal of the Linnean Society* **96**: 57-68.

Winchester, V. and Chaujar, R.K. (2002) Lichenometric dating of slope movements, Nant Ffrancon, North Wales. *Geomorphology* **47**: 61-74.

16. Thornthwaite Force – the Otter Stone

On the trail of a wild otter

Checklist:

Distance: 1 mile.

Ascent: Negligible.

Approximate Time: Allow one hour.

Maps: 1:25 000 OS Explorer OL5.
1:50 000 OS Landranger 90.

Terrain: Level, woodland and riverside paths, occasionally boggy.

Equipment and Books: Camera and a hand lens.

Footwear: Boots or wellingtons.

Special Considerations: Please leave the area with the otter spraints as you found it for others to see.

Parking: Burnbanks (NY508161).

Public Transport: Buses from Penrith to Burnbanks. NMB Hire Service 111 'The Haweswater Rambler'.

Refreshments: Haweswater Hotel.

Ask someone which British wild animal they would most like to see, and the most-likely answer would be a golden eagle or an otter. You can, of course, see them on TV, but to see them in the wild is quite another matter. Most visitors to Haweswater know of the golden eagles at Riggindale but few are aware of the otters.

This walk will not guarantee a sighting but during this brief hour, with a bit of luck, you will find the signs. Otters mark their territory at specific sites. To other otters, the signs are clear at a distance: the signals are in the scent. For us humans, who rely so much on eyesight, the signs are more difficult to find.

This walk is only one mile in total, there and back. On it, there is one particular site where otters regularly leave their mark – droppings or more technically, 'spraints'. The location is given in the 'Solutions' section. And so, if you want to have a go at tracking down a wild otter, look away from the Solutions section now… and follow the route about to be described!

Begin at the village of Burnbanks. The roadside parking-area is on the edge of the Navvy Camp built by Manchester Corporation for the purpose of building the Haweswater Dam. In 1939 there were 40 prefabricated buildings that included a mission hall, a recreation hall with stage, a canteen, dispensary and shop. The 1930s' Depression stopped work for four years but when it resumed in 1935, Burnbanks village had a population of 400. In 1940 the village was dismantled leaving only eleven houses and the 'staff bungalows'.

The walk starts at a roadside gate (signpost Naddle Bridge). Fifty metres into the woodland and approximately five metres to the right of the path there is a rectangular **concrete foundation** – all that remains of one of the dismantled 'prefabs'. Hidden in undergrowth to the left, is the foundation of the mission hall.

Continue following the narrow woodland path between mature oaks with a ground cover of greater stitchwort, wood sorrel and bluebells. Before reaching the stile that leads onto the road, look across to the right, down to the water's edge to see an extensive area of wild garlic, This plant is taken for granted in the gardens and driveways of Keswick – even regarded as a weed. It indicates high levels of calcium, belonging to a group of plants known to botanists as 'calcicoles'.

Return to the path and cross the steep ladder stile onto the road. You are now on the modern Naddle Bridge built in 1936 to take the new road up the valley. Cross the road and take the ladder stile opposite, down onto the old 'road' that used to lead to Mardale. To the left you can see the remnants of the old trackway. To the right you cross the old Naddle Bridge. It is only four and a half feet wide and has no parapet: a forgotten packhorse bridge, dwarfed by its new neighbour that shoulders-up alongside. Motorists miss all this for it is completely hidden from their view.

After crossing the old bridge, the path turns left across a wooden footbridge. It all seems disproportionate for the size of the streams that are being crossed. Firstly, the new road bridge has two massive arches, and the Haweswater Beck only flows through one – the other appearing permanently dry and unnecessary. And now, the wooden footbridge crosses over a small steam that is almost lost in its broad riverbed. The bridges say 'massive flows': the streams in actuality say 'just a trickle'. This is a puzzle that will present itself many times during this walk.

Twenty metres past the wooden footbridge you cross a plank 'bridge' and then reach an electricity transmission pole guyed with two steel cables. Follow the line of the furthest guy-line down to the river edge. On the 20th April 2002, on a flat coffin-shaped stone just up from the water's edge, I found an otter spraint. It was black and slimy and contained frog vertebrae and fish vertebrae – you can tell the difference – in frogs the ends of the vertebrae are concave and convex whilst in fish they are both concave (Figure 16.1). The rock was bare apart from the spraint, which meant that this site was not often used. I've been back several times since

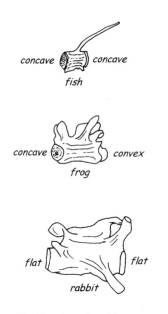

concave   concave

fish

concave   convex

frog

flat   flat

rabbit

Figure 16.1 Vertebrae found in otter spraints

then and have not found any fresh signs, but of course it is still worth checking. You may be lucky.

What you really need to be looking for is a similar rock but with masses of tell-tale green algae spreading out from a focal point. After many years of use, concentric zones of algae and lichen develop due to the continuous application of nitrates and phosphates.

If you follow the line of the other guy-line down to the waterside, there is a boulder covered in moss, and a dog lichen with horizontal chestnut-coloured discs (*Peltigera horizontalis*). The lichen is interesting because it shows that this area has a link with the 'old forests' that used to cover most of Britain.

Further on, the river bank appears to bear no relation to the present river level. It seems a remnant of former days when the water level was much higher. In April and early May in this marshy area you will find marsh marigolds in flower. A strange plant this, for behind the flower there appears to be no sepals (the parts that enclose the flower before it opens). But close inspection reveals a flower that is made up *only* of sepals – it is the petals that are missing!

The path continues across a small outflow from a spring before reaching a steep ladder stile in a stone wall. Before crossing the wall, drop down left to look at the former river-bed. Here is a bar of resistant volcanic rock that forms the waterfall known as Thornthwaite Force. The waterfall is not high on the list of tourist attractions but at one time it would have been a far more dramatic sight. Only half the waterfall remains. The part you are standing on, between the edge of the wall and an isolated oak, used to be the other half, pouring over the rock ledge in front of you. Look closely at the surface of the rocks here. They are smoothed-out into scallop shapes, indicating many years of torrential flow. All that remains now is a dried-up mossy pavement.

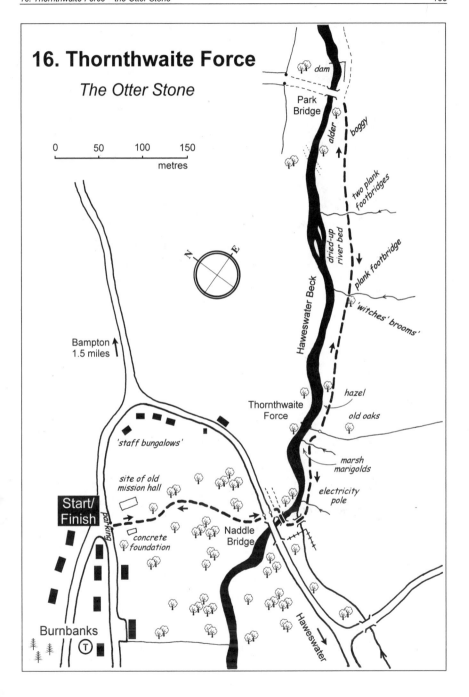

Thornthwaite Force – now only half its size since the building of the Haweswater Dam.

Cross the stile and drop down to examine more closely the missing half of Thornthwaite Force. To confirm the change that has taken place, look at the lichen colonies where the water once flowed, and compare them with the unwashed rock outcrops on each side. The largest colonies from the 'lost' waterfall measure 80mm. On the rock buttress that would have formed the edge of the original fall, the same colonies measure 360mm.

The last time I was here, there was a family of mallard and a dipper along this section. Seventy metres further, the path goes past a grassy area with some exceptionally large ant-hills, some up to half a metre in diameter. Look out also in this area for a large downy birch covered in **'witches' brooms'**. These are caused by the fungus, *Exoascus turgidus*, which produces rapid cell development in the tree's tissue. Some of the growths act as aerial tree nurseries – hanging baskets covered in moss and young birch seedlings.

You cross a railway sleeper. Keep looking for otter signs. Sometimes the spraints may be left on a prominent patch of grass. Over time a raised dome may develop covered in dark-green grass that is often left ungrazed by sheep. Bridges are also good places to check.

Once over the sleeper 'bridge', notice the **dried-up river bed** with islands of trees. The path crosses a boggy section, over stepping-stones and two more sleeper bridges. There is a line of old alders and then you reach Park Bridge. A sign tells you that you are on the 'Coast to Coast Walk'. What chance our otter now on such a well-trodden route?

Ahead of you lies Robin Hood's Bay, but this is the furthest point we reach on this walk. Before turning back, drop down to look under the bridge. It is worthwhile checking under bridges, for these are often quiet places where an otter would feel more secure.

If you have no luck in your search here, you can always examine the liverwort growing down at the base of the stonework. *Conocephalum conicum* means 'cone-head' in Latin (derived from the shape of its spore capsules). The plant can be easily identified by examining the surface

with a x10 hand lens, which reveals a pattern of hexagonal cells, each with a central pore. It has an antiseptic smell when bruised.

Retrace your steps back to Thornthwaite Force, but before crossing the stile, look across to your left to a pair of **old oaks**. This is a good place for lunch and to ponder on the origin of these ancient trees. Are they two separate trees? Is it one tree that has split in two, or one tree where the middle has rotted away? The two trunks have been attacked by insects and have developed a thick blanket of swollen burrs. The higher branches are covered in polypody fern.

Before moving on, drop down to the river

Ancient oaks near Thornthwaite Force. Are these separate trees or one tree split in two?

once again. Down-stream are two massive oaks, overhanging the water, each covered in polypody. Immediately up-stream there is a small hazel. Look carefully around its base where the roots form overgrown hollows. Look for hazelnuts that have been gnawed by a wood mouse – you may find one with individual teeth marks on the outer casing.

Now you should be ready for the final section, back over the stile, along the riverside path and back to the road bridge.

If you haven't found any otter spraint by the time you reach the road then turn to the 'Solutions' section, and all will be revealed!

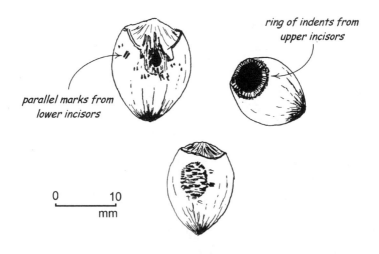

Figure 16.2 Hazelnuts gnawed by a wood mouse

Taking it Further

The reduced water flow in Haweswater Beck followed the construction of the reservoir. The new Naddle Bridge was built before completion of the dam, and the two massive arches were necessary to take the large volume of water that originally flowed through. Today, the constant removal of water means that only one arch of the bridge has water flowing under it. You could say that Manchester has taken away the missing half of Thornthwaite Force!

There is, however, a long history of interference with the flow of water in Haweswater Beck. Evidence from historical documents and old maps shows a river with numerous mills, dams and weirs. An early sketch map of the area between Naddle Bridge and Park Bridge (thought to be early nineteenth century – see James Parnel) has the following field names: Grindstone Close, Mill How, Thornthwaite Mill and Mill Hill (a pre-1858 mill). Old OS maps (1st and 2nd edition) show the positions of weirs and dams.

Place-names on maps also indicate the past association of the area with otters and fish. On modern maps there is an 'Otter Bank' south of Rosgill (NY537161). On the OS 1st edition 6" map (1863), an 'Eel Coup' is shown east of Naddle Bridge alongside a weir, suggesting a site where eels were being trapped (eels are a favourite prey for otters). The name 'Guerness' on the east shore of Haweswater also suggests that this was an area with good fish stocks. Guerness means 'a fish trap headland' from the Old English *grin, giran* or *geren* meaning 'trap' (Smith, 1967, 2, 167). 'Naddle' may be derived from Old Norse *naddr* and *dalr* meaning 'pointed valley', or from the Shetland dialect language Norn where *naddi* is a type of fish (Smith, 1967, 2, 169).

Bibliography

Burnbanks village plans *c.*1939, Scale 1": 40ft. Haweswater Dam Construction Photographic Archive: 4152/2. North West Water, Watergate Treatment Plant, Kendal.

Lowther, Lords Lonsdale: Plans/L/Westmorland/Box/Bampton/27. Carlisle Records Office.

Ordnance Survey 1st edition 6": 1 mile. (1863), Southampton.

Parnell, J. (no date) Sketch Plan of Naddle Estate. Cumbrian Records Office.

Smith, A. H. (1967), The place-names of Westmorland, **2**, English Place-name Society, Cambridge.

17. Pooley Bridge – the Dunmallard Ash

A Meeting with one of Cumbria's largest trees

Checklist:

Distance: 1.3 miles.

Ascent: 130ft (40m).

Approximate Time: Allow 1 hour.

Maps: 1:25 000 OS Explorer OL5.
1:50 000 OS Landranger 90.1:250 000
British Geological Survey, 54N 04W Lake
District.

Terrain: Gentle woodland and riverside
paths.

Equipment and Books: Tape measure,
camera.

Footwear: Walking shoes are adequate in
dry weather.

Special Considerations: This walk is
worth doing if only to see the 'Dunmallard
Ash'.

Parking: Pooley Bridge (NY469245).

Public Transport: Buses from Carlisle to
Penrith and Patterdale, Stagecoach
Service 108. Penrith to Pooley Bridge,
Royal Mail Postbus Service 110.

Refreshments: Pooley Bridge.

From the car park I took the path that contoured around the south side of the hill. The wood was mostly beech, and in spring has a ground cover of dog's mercury, wild arum, garlic, bluebells and wood anemones. The geology map showed I was walking over gravel-like material, probably laid down in river deposits about 400 million years ago. It produces characteristically rounded hills such as Little Mell Fell and Great Mell Fell (the deposits are named 'Mell Fell Conglomerates'). One of the consequences of this particular geology is a reduction in the amount of available rock suitable for building walls. Most of the fields are enclosed by wire fences. Before this, the boundaries were hedgerows, banks and ditches.

The path continued rising gently. The beech trees had been planted in straight lines converging on the summit. Initially they had been planted close together, and since then, every two rows in between the existing rows had been felled to allow space to mature. As I continued over the west side, there were increasing **signs of rabbits**. The Mell Fell Conglomerates produce a sandy and well-drained subsoil – ideal for burrowing.

Some of the **exposed tree roots** at the side of the path had been gnawed. The elder trees in particular had received special attention. Some had had their bark removed along a six-inch-wide band at ground

Tree base gnawed by rabbits (© Howard Holden 2003)

level. Some had the characteristic marks of a rabbit's top incisors (see photograph alongside). The two incisor teeth produce four parallel grooves. This is due to each tooth having a notch in its cutting edge. There were also rabbit droppings that had been left on the tops of some of the sawn-off **tree stumps**. This is a characteristic practice of rabbits, which use their droppings to mark their territory.

On reaching the north side of the hill, the fence was replaced by a puzzling section of sandstone wall. Why had such a short section been built on this side of the hill? And why had someone planted a row of **cupressus** in front of it? A few metres further, I reached a gate where I was able to look out across the fields below.

A faint track led down to a stile over a hedge and fence, and then across another field to a stile with a white post. Once over this far stile, I turned right to follow the fence in the direction of the river.

I passed two **large oaks** growing along the field boundary. Each had patches of yellow 'dust' within the cracks of the bark. With a x10 hand lens, the yellow surface appeared as a crust of minute granules, each less than 0.1mm in diameter. This was the lichen *Chrysothrix candelaris*, which favours shaded cracks in acid-barked trees, particularly oak. After approximately 150 metres, I reached a gate with a two-metre high **sandstone pillar** supporting its hinges. Its companion post was laid flat alongside the fence (16 metres to the south). The first and second edition OS maps show an old field boundary at this point that takes a curved line back towards the river. I passed through the gate to follow it. I found myself walking along a sunken trackway. On my right was a line of wind-swept trees that would once have formed an ancient **hedgerow**. The first three trees were hollow alders – decaying fragments but still alive. Next was an old oak followed by three hawthorns that were used as rubbing posts. The soil around their roots had been eroded away by visiting sheep. Then I came to a giant of a tree – an ancient ash. This tree has a diameter of 229cm and has been officially recorded as the second largest ash in Cumbria (the largest is at Penny Bridge with a diameter of 236cm). But such statistics do not do justice to this tree. British tree measure-

ments are taken by TROBI (The Tree Register of the British Isles) who specify that the measurements be taken 1.5 metres above ground level. This ash expands its girth dramatically at ground level and at this height, its circumference is almost 40ft! This ranks closely with the British Champion Ash, which has a girth of 57ft.

This was a strange place. The ancient curved track seemed to be leading nowhere. A local archaeologist believes that it may represent the site of a Roman harbour that brought supplies to a Roman fort built on the slope above (Bell 2001). There is evidence of an **old wall**

The Dunmallard Ash (© Howard Holden 2003)

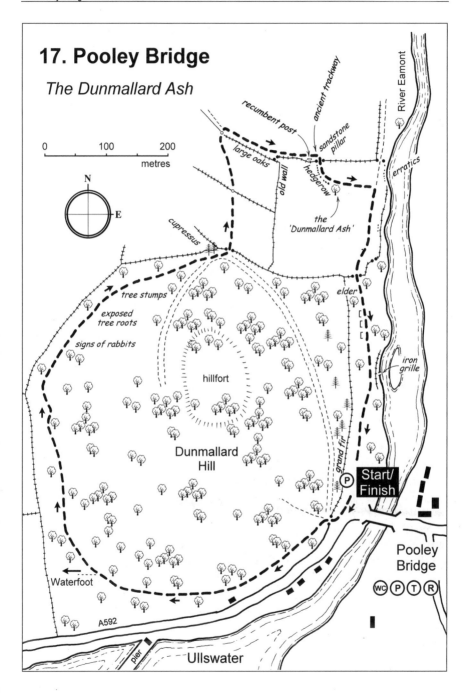

17. Pooley Bridge

The Dunmallard Ash

constructed of dressed sandstone that would have formed the fort's eastern rampart. This all sounds extremely speculative. But perhaps in its defence, it is worth remembering that these stones are likely to have been transported long distances to reach this site. Would such effort have been expended on building a simple field wall?

As I dropped down towards the river, I noticed five boulders along the riverbank. These were ice-smoothed **erratics** of Borrowdale Volcanic rock. I made my way along the riverside path. The steeply-sloping field to the right was a favourite place for rabbits. Where the soil had been disturbed and thrown out from a burrow entrance, there were lines of thistles (mostly *Cirsium vulgare*). Thistles are frequently found on freshly-exposed soil. They are opportunist plants, and their efficient seed dispersal and rapid growth means that they quickly exploit bare ground. It was late afternoon, in full daylight, and yet I was able to approach within ten metres of a rabbit before it ran away. From past observations, in areas where there is a high buzzard population, rabbits will disappear underground almost immediately on seeing a predator. For this population, in May 2003, there would seem to be few, if any, natural enemies. Consequently, they showed no fear.

The grassy path led through a gate. Five metres past the gate, I noticed an **elder** infected with the velvety wine-coloured fungus, *Auricularia auricula-judae*. The common name for this fungus is 'Jew's ear' because it is found on elder – the tree on which Judas Iscariot was thought to have hanged himself.

The sheltered path continued past an island just out from the riverbank. It was shaped like an aerofoil section of an aircraft wing, with an artificial edge built of concrete and stone. The riverbank that forms the side of the narrow through-channel was similarly constructed. A careful inspection, looking over the protective wooden handrail, revealed the exit of a water tunnel covered by an **iron grille**. This is part of the 'compensation arrangement' built to maintain the water level in the river when water is being extracted from Ullswater across into Haweswater. Without it, the river would effectively stop flowing and this upper section would become toxic through lack of oxygen.

I was nearly back at my starting point when I noticed the occasional **grand fir** (*Abies grandis*) on the right of the path and along the side of the car park. Firs can be difficult to identify but this one has a secret – bruising its leaves gently between the fingers releases the tell-tale smell of oranges!

Taking it Further

For more information on 'Champion Trees', contact TROBI (E-mail: trobi@aol.com).

The recording of trees is becoming more accurate, using laser technology to measure height instead of trigonometry and tape measures. There is a problem when measuring girth, in deciding the height above ground level at which to take the measurements. *English Nature* state that girth should be measured at 1.3 metres above ground level whilst TROBI state 1.5 metres. A matter of 0.2 metres may seem trivial, but to an ash tree like the one at Dunmallard, it can make all the difference as to whether it is a 'Champion' or not!

The massive base of the Dunmallard Ash. Recording of tree girth is traditionally taken at chest height, but this does not take into account the expansion at ground level. (© Howard Holden 2003)

Bibliography

Bell, T.C (2001) *Dunmallard, Pooley Bridge: The Roman Occupation.* Unpublished typescript.

18. Carrock Fell – The Last Outpost

An archaeological and geological excursion

Checklist:

Distance: 3.5 miles.

Ascent: 1400ft (420m).

Approximate Time: 3 to 4 hours.

Maps: 1:25 000 OS Explorer OL4.
1:50 000 OS Landranger 89 or 90.
1:50 000 British Geological Survey,
England and Wales Sheet 23,
Cockermouth.

Terrain: Little-used paths. Steep ascent followed by traverse of exposed heather moor. The descent to Mosedale is steep over loose scree.

Equipment and Books: Hand lens, compass. *Lakeland Geology* by E. H. Shackleton gives a comprehensive geological account of the area.

Footwear: Boots.

Special Considerations: Route-finding across the southern slope of Carrock Fell could be difficult in mist.

Parking: Ample space on roadside 200 metres north of Stone Ends (NY353337).

Public Transport: Buses from Keswick to Carlisle. Stagecoach Service 73/73A, 'Caldbeck Rambler' passes Mosedale and Stone Ends.

Refreshments: Mosedale Tea Room (Quaker Meeting House) – Open late June to early September.

I parked the car on the roadside, 200 metres north of the farm at Stone Ends. Making sense of the east side of Carrock Fell was the first challenge. Volcanic magma that solidifies underground is called 'plutonic' from 'Pluto' the king of the Underworld. Carrock Fell is made up from two different plutonic rocks: granite and gabbro. Looking up at the cliff face in front of me, gabbro was to the left, granite to the right, and the fault down the middle was filled with 'diorite', which geologists define as being intermediate between the two.

I followed the path around the edge of a shallow quarry and climbed gently through a landscape of pink granite boulders. My route was to follow the line of weakness marked by the diorite. The path headed through bracken towards an area of loose scree.

I zigzagged up the right-hand edge avoiding most of the loose stones. The acid soil on each side of the path was being colonised by parsley fern and bilberries. After this difficult section the path led to a solitary **rowan** growing on a prominent rock outcrop. Looking directly down from here to a spot 20 to 30 metres up from the road, I could see evidence of an ancient 'settlement'. Two structures were clearly visible: one forming a circle; the other a rectangle.

I continued my ascent with Further Gill Sike now close on my left. The path climbed a miniature **dry valley** formed along the seam of diorite. I looked down at the dry grass surface. It had been worn into a series of **boot prints** like tracks made in snow!

Sherlock Holmes would have enjoyed this:

"Where else in the Lake District have you seen *this*, Watson?"

"I can't think, Holmes."

"*Nowhere* else, Watson! It's too perfect. Normally, footpaths are so heavily used, they are just worn away in a haphazard manner. But this has every boot print left intact."

"Well it's a quiet area … and its very steep, and people just follow in the steps that others have made."

"Alright Watson – what happens when you come down?"

"I wouldn't come down this way."

"Exactly! – my dear friend."

Where the path had eroded through the grass, I could see the underlying diorite. The geology map describes it as 'ferrodiorite'. Its speckled surface was partially stained with iron oxide, and it felt heavy. Further ahead, the path took a narrow channel through tall heather. It then levelled out before reaching a **sheepfold**. This was built from the pink microgranite I stood inside the main rectangular structure. In the middle of the east-facing wall, one metre up, was a grey crust covered in what looked like spots of blood. This was a particular striking lichen with the equally-striking name – *Haematomma ventosum* – the translation being: 'blood-red eyes made sore by the wind'.

The path continued along a gentle slope, past two cairns, across a sheep track and then an area of stunted *Calluna* heath with patches of crowberry. The path then crossed a jumble of small boulders covered in the moss *Rhacomitrium lanuginosum*. This particular moss is found mostly on level mountain tops or tundra. It colonises horizontal surfaces because it lacks the root-like structures to hold onto upright surfaces. The leaf tips have long hair-like points covered in microscopic lumps. These appear as hoary white wisps as soon as the air turns dry, which gives it the name: 'woolly-hair moss' or 'frizzy-hair moss'.

I reached the cairn marking the top of this mass of boulders. From here I could see the summit plateau and the eastern rampart of the ancient hill fort. This was a real puzzle. The Carrock Fell fort has been described as the largest Iron Age hill fort in Cumbria, ranking in size with the one on Ingleburgh and with many in Scotland. It was surveyed in 1938 by Collingwood and very little has been added to our knowledge of the site since then. The objective facts are only what you see on the ground today. The rest is speculation: built by a northern tribe known as the Brigantes; the walls would have reached a height sufficient for defence (at least as tall as they are wide); there may have been dwellings set inside the protective perimeter, built of wood and thatch and hence have left no trace; the Romans over-ran the site and 'slighted' it by casting down the walls so that it could no longer be used. The oval pile of stones that has been hollowed-out to form a shelter is thought to have been a funerary cairn. Its contents, including a stone cist, have been robbed-out.

With all this in mind, I crossed over the boulder-strewn ground to enter at the eastern gateway. The neat-looking section of wall on the right of the entrance is too neat and clean to be original. I continued across to examine the remains of the **funerary cairn** and then cut across to the first gap in the north wall. This was one of the strategic sections thought to have been dismantled by the Romans. This side of the fort was sheltered from the prevailing south-westerly winds and the slight difference in exposure had led to an increase in heather and crowberry. The area was one of the few parts of the Lake District that still had the feel of 'tundra' about it. I continued along the outside of the wall. It was covered in *Rhacomitrium* moss. On reaching the second gap, I found the **'reindeer lichens'** – *Cladonia impexa* and *C. arbuscula*. Both of these are used as miniature trees by architects and model railway enthusiasts. *Cladonia arbuscula* has even the appearance of being shaped by the wind, with all its branches dragged out in one direction (see Figure 18.1). The next section of wall is probably the best preserved of the original. The inner and outer courses can be seen made of larger stones supporting an infill of smaller pieces.

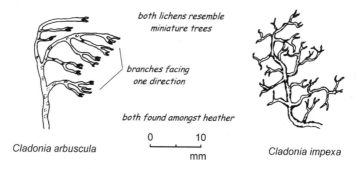

both lichens resemble miniature trees

branches facing one direction

both found amongst heather

0   10
mm

Cladonia arbuscula   *Cladonia impexa*

Figure 18.1 'Reindeer lichens' from the summit plateau of Carrock Fell

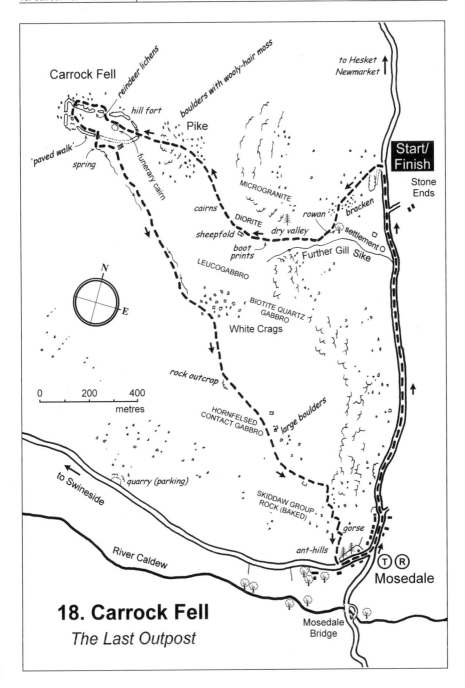

Carrock Fell

reindeer lichens

hill fort

Pike

boulders with wooly-hair moss

to Hesket
Newmarket

Start/
Finish

Stone
Ends

'paved walk'

spring

funerary cairn

MICROGRANITE

cairns

DIORITE

sheepfold

boot
prints

LEUCOGABBRO

dry valley

rowan

bracken

settlement O

Further Gill Sike

N

E

BIOTITE QUARTZ
GABBRO

White Crags

0   200   400
metres

rock outcrop

HORNFELSED
CONTACT GABBRO

large boulders

to Swineside

quarry (parking)

SKIDDAW GROUP
ROCK (BAKED)

gorse

ant-hills

River Caldew

(T) (R)
Mosedale

18. Carrock Fell
The Last Outpost

Mosedale
Bridge

Where the wall runs up to a natural rock outcrop, I climbed back inside and made my way to examine the western gate. It was difficult to distinguish between the natural rock and those boulders moved deliberately to form part of the defensive wall. After crossing the summit with its modern shelter, I followed the line of the southern wall. Up until now, all the walls of the fort had been built of microgranite but on this southern side of the summit plateau, I was approaching the seam of diorite that I had seen on the way up. Most of the wall was pink microgranite, but here and there were signs of the speckled ferrodiorite All that was left of this south wall was a low foundation with a middle infill that was bedded together with smaller stones and covered in *Rhacomitrium* moss. Collingwood suggested that this may have been a **'paved walk'** on top of the original wall.

I continued along the south side until I reached another gap – the south gate. Of all the gaps in the fort, this one would seem to have a definite purpose. Thirty metres out from the gap, I came to the fort's water supply. This was a fast-flowing spring on what appeared to be the junction of the diorite and the gabbro. Thirty metres to reach the only running water on the plateau: that was a puzzle. If you were building a fort to withstand an attack and a possible siege, you would incorporate the water supply *within* your defences rather than leave it to the enemy.

I returned to the south wall to briefly follow the remaining section. It had been almost completely robbed-out to build the sheepfold. From here I was able to join a faint path heading south-east, roughly following the line taken by the stream that had emerged from the spring. I was about to cross an area that, on the surface, looked to be quite uniform with its covering of heather. But geologically, I was about to cross a sequence of plutonic rocks that would take me through the middle of a hidden field of magma. The rocks were about to become lighter in colour as the iron content was replaced by quartz. Approximately 100 metres after leaving the sheepfold the gabbro began to appear as scattered outcrops and isolated boulders. The geology map indicated that I was crossing a band of 'leucogabbro' – from the Greek: *leukos* for 'white'. The texture was unmistakably gabbro – good for rock climbing – so good, it won't let go of your boots!

The path dropped down through a wet section with sphagnum and rushes. The stream kept appearing alongside the path as intermittent runnels. And then I came to the area marked on the map as 'White Crags'. Suddenly, the rocks had changed. All about me were white angular rocks lying on the dark heather like a sprinkling of giant sugar crystals.

Another glance at the geology map indicated 'biotite quartz gabbro'. And there it was! I could see the quartz crystals glistening white, and the black biotite crystals weathering out on the surface.

I continued along the narrow path as it cut its way across the gentle slopes of heather. Approximately 400 metres after leaving the White Crags, I passed a small **rock outcrop** to the right of the path. Things were changing rapidly on the geology map. I had now reached a band described as 'hornfelsed contact gabbro'. This was gabbro at the edge of the main plutonic mass. In a molten mix, one of the first minerals to come out of solution is iron (leaving the quartz to solidify later). This was it: the gabbro was full of iron. The evidence was in the darker colour, and it was heavier than the 'white gabbro'. It was also covered in different lichens.

From the outcrop, I could see a group of **large boulders** about 400 metres away, lying just to the left of the path. Bits of these rocks had been chipped away so I knew I was onto something! I quickly clambered to the top of the largest rock. I was expecting all the lichens associated with a bird-perching site and I wasn't disappointed. But this rock had some interesting differences. Instead of the usual 'crottle' (*Parmelia saxatilis*), there was *P. omphalodes*, or what people in the north-west of Scotland call 'dark crottle'. This lichen was collected in the past for dying Harris Tweed. It produces a golden brown dye which gives the wool a distinctive aroma when wet. The other lichen associated with such isolated

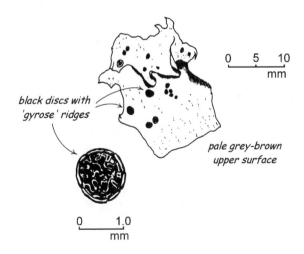

black discs with 'gyrose' ridges

pale grey-brown upper surface

Figure 18.2 *Umbilicaria torrefacta* on gabbro boulders enriched with bird droppings

perching sites is 'rock tripe' – yet another lichen dye. Incidentally, those lichens that have been traditionally collected for dyes or herbal remedies have been given common English names. The rest have been left to Latin – for lichen anoraks to mull over! And so, true to type, I took out my hand lens and kneeled down on the top to examine some grey-brown crinkled leaves…

"*Umbilicaria torrefacta.*" – enough said!

I rejoined the path. It had become increasingly narrow as it cut through the tall heather. A large cairn marked the high ground on the right but the path continued straight ahead to a sheep shelter. From here the easy gradients suddenly gave way to a steep decent over increasingly loose scree. The gabbro had ended and I was about to cross over onto Skiddaw Group rock that had been baked hard and brittle by contact with the younger plutonic rock. It made for a tricky decent over a loose, friable stair-way. And then, for the first time on this walk, I noticed the view. I could have been in an aeroplane looking down over the hamlet of Mosedale; heading out across the two bridges; along the edge of the Lake

"… for the first time on this walk, I noticed the view. I could have been in an aeroplane looking down over the hamlet of Mosedale …"

District to Great Mell Fell and beyond. From here, this really did seem like the last outpost – a place you would build a hill fort – a place you would want to defend.

Half-way down, the path crossed an area of gorse before descending into tall bracken. I aimed for the right-hand corner of a walled enclosure planted with larch. To the right was a grass slope with ant-hills. Directly below was the road leading down the valley from Swineside. I joined the road and continued through the village, turning left to follow the road north, back to my starting point and the car.

Taking it Further

This part of the Lake District provides an opportunity of studying the field relationships of different rocks and plants: to match the minerology to the flora. The rationale for such work already exists in botany where it is known as 'phytosociology' – the grouping together of plants associated with a particular habitat. Lichenologists are familiar with this approach and recognise a number of lichen communities, each with their own respective 'alliances'. There is, for example, a separate alliance for exposed siliceous rock that is enriched with bird droppings. Within this community, the same lichens keep appearing, amongst which are certain *Umbilicaria* species as well as *Parmelia saxatilis* and *P. omphalodes*. A full account of this approach together with a list of lichen communities found in the British Isles is given in James, Hawksworth and Rose (1977). Lists of lichens associated with different types of 'acid' rocks can be found in Gilbert (2000).

The geology of Carrock Fell offers a fascinating study of how lichens colonise a sequence of plutonic rocks. As you cross the fell, the chemistry of the magma changes. The rapidly-chilled edges are said to be 'mafic' – rich in ferromagnesian minerals. These were the first rocks to solidify at this high initial temperature. Minerals have a fixed position in a series that crystallise out at precise temperatures as the magma cools. The final mix is described as being 'felsic' – rich in feldspar and silica. As you pass from mafic to felsic, the rocks become more acidic. Directly in contact with this landscape are the lichens.

There are many ecological factors that need to be recorded when mapping the distribution of lichen on these rocks. These include height above ground, orientation, inclination, degree of shelter, whether the rock is part of a cluster of rocks or isolated, previous land management such as heather burning, and eutrophication from birds and sheep.

As well as the differences in rock chemistry, such a study could also

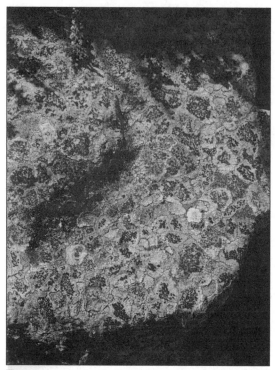

The regular mosaic of crustose lichen found on hornfelsed gabbro

take account of rock texture and crystal alignment. Skiddaw Group rock retains a distinct bedding plane (as well as a superimposed cleavage plane) and many of the *Rhizocarpon* colonies will follow a particular axis. In contrast, the *Rhizocarpon* colonies of the quartz-rich gabbro are mostly circular.

There are many puzzles. Why for example, do lichens on the hornfelsed gabbro form regular mosaics? Could it be the extreme slow growth caused by the hard, impervious surface that stops any one colony from dominating the others?

Bibliography

Collingwood, R.G (1938) The hill fort on CarrockFell. *Transactions of the Cumberland and Westmorland Antiquary and Archaeological Society.* **XXXVIII** (New Series): 32-41.

Gilbert, O.L. (2000) *Lichens*: 95-117. HarperCollins.

James, P. W., Hawksworth, D. L. and Rose, F. (1977) Lichen communities in the British Isles: a preliminary conspectus. In *Lichen Ecology* (Seaward, M. R. D., ed.) 295-413. Academic Press, London.

Shackleton, E.H (1966) *Lakeland Geology*: 57-60. Dalesman Publications.

Solutions

1. Loweswater

The pheasant in winter (© Howard Holden 2003)

Holme Wood was planted in the 1950s in the shape of a pheasant. The head points towards the south-east (facing left in the photograph), and can be distinguished by the circular patch of larch that represents the eye. The best time to see it is in December when the larch is turning gold, and the pheasant is in bright winter plumage!

2. Buttermere

The alluvial flat that characterises this end of Buttermere provides a fertile pasture for large numbers of sheep and cattle. The level fields have frequently been 'harrowed' to improve the land for livestock. The surviving ant population has found the one piece of ground that is safe from trampling and mechanical disturbance – under the wire fence. Smart ants!

The best examples of iron wire affecting lichens can be found on fenceposts alongside forest plantations in north-west Scotland.

3. Newlands Valley

The dominant factor is the rusty galvanised wire! Look closely where the staple is attached. The iron and zinc oxides are leaching into the wood, and where they drain down the wood surface – no growth can be seen.

4. Castlerigg Stone Circle

This field once contained a hidden 'relic' that could be discovered using the position of the surrounding stones. In 1984, a 'crème-egg' was buried in the centre of the circle, as part of a popular treasure hunt competition!

5. Walla Crag

The rowan had eight strands of wire stapled to its trunk. The 1:25 000 OS map confirmed the evidence. Two black lines were drawn on the map following the footpath. One line marked the wall: the other marked where an eight-strand wire fence had been fixed to the trees instead of using fence posts!

6. Combe Gill

What has caused the circular patterns in the grass? The answer is revealed during spring and early summer. The grass contains thistles, and as they grow, the spreading rosettes of spiky leaves stop the sheep from grazing around their edges. What is surprising is that the circles of tall grass remain even after the second year, when the biennial thistles have died back.

The underside of the arch shows a distinct join in the stonework where the original bridge was widened.

7. Eskdale

"… the country doctor owns a horse and trap." Look closely at the underside of the arch. There is a join in the stonework showing where the original packhorse bridge was widened in 1734. This was to allow Doctor Edward Tyson to cross over to see his patients. There are many examples in the Lake District of bridges on busy routes having been widened (Wha House Bridge is an example further up the valley), but this bridge across the Esk leads only to the quiet farmsteads of Penny Hill and Low Birker. Dr Tyson certainly made his authority count.

8. Devoke Water

The iron rod projecting through the plywood base is one of many that can be found in this sheep-farming area. Its purpose is to hold in position a 'mineral block' that provides minerals, such as magnesium, lacking in the hill sheep's diet. The surrounding vegetation is affected as the block dissolves away into the nearby soil. There is also a manuring affect from sheep that visit the site.

11. Whitbarrow

The patch of smaller lichens is where the rock was chipped away. The lichen diameters would indicate that this happened about 30 years ago, possibly by an over-enthusiastic geologist wishing to confirm the origin of this volcanic erratic.

12. Fairfield

The padlocked iron gates are 'track gates' built into the walls so that engineers can walk the path taken by the Thirlmere aqueduct. The straight line changes direction at a point just east of Brockstone where it continues along a bearing of 80 degrees across the south face of Nab Scar. The stone slab marks the highest point on the route.

15. Haweswater

The stone ball from the top right-hand corner of the church roof (see photograph of model) can be seen on top of the wall above the post-box. The church windows were used in the sides of the octagonal draw-off tower.

If you examine the 1:25 000 OS map at grid reference NY477097, a stone is marked 'BS' for boundary stone. The letter 'L' carved on the stone stands for Longsleddale: 'H' for Haweswater (at some date the stone has been reversed). The OS map shows that the fence follows the old Parish boundary. Before the erection of such fences, the ancient manor boundaries were often disputed, particularly where there was no obvious geographical line such as a river or a ridge. In such cases, a line of stones, or 'currocks', were placed along an agreed boundary (see Winchester 2000). This may explain the line of stones left underneath the fence on the rather featureless slope of Branstree.

16. Thornthwaite Force

Look closely under both arches of the road bridge. Look for stones that support a covering of green algae. If you are lucky, you should see fresh otter spraints.

Bridges are good places to check for spraints. They offer seclusion and relative security for the otter. They also provide shelter from the weather, and spraints are less likely to be washed away by direct exposure to rain.

These photographs were taken in April 2003, when otter spraints were found under both arches of the road bridge.

Index

Also of Interest:

WALKS IN ANCIENT LAKELAND
Robert Harris
Enjoy a 'Walk in Ancient Lakeland' and discover sites and monuments from the Neolithic and Bronze Ages you never knew existed. Discover the great stone circles, standing stones and burial cairns which still decorate these beautiful hills. Follow the ancient trackways linking these ancient sites and explore largely unknown areas to uncover the mysteries of the lives of our ancestors in this timeless landscape. *£7.95*

WALKING THE WAINWRIGHTS
Stuart Marshall
This ground-breaking book is a scheme of walks linking all the 214 peaks in the late Alfred Wainwright's seven-volume 'Pictorial Guide to The Lakeland Fells'. After an introduction to the Lake District, the route descriptions are clearly presented with the two-colour sketch maps facing the descriptive text – so that the book can be carried flat in a standard map case. The walks average 12 miles in length but the more demanding ones are presented both as one-day and two-day excursions. *£7.95*

WATERSIDE WALKS IN THE LAKE DISTRICT
Colin Shelbourn
A unique compilation of 25 walks around and alongside a selection of the many water features to be found in this favourite walking area – lakes, tarns, becks, rivers and waterfalls. Ranging from 1 to 16 km, from gentle strolls to more strenuous hikes there are suitable walks for all age groups. Each walk includes information about parking, the length of the walk, a clear map to guide you, the level of difficulty, some very interesting facts of particular relevance and many beautiful photographs. *£7.95*

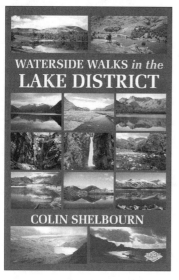

All of our books are available through booksellers. In case of difficulty, or for a free catalogue, please contact: **SIGMA LEISURE, 5 ALTON ROAD, WILMSLOW, CHESHIRE SK9 6AR.**
Phone/fax: 01625-531035
E-mail: info@sigmapress.co.uk
Web site: www.sigmapress.co.uk